*Enjoy the fastest growing hobby in Canada!*

# Trace your Family Tree

A DO-IT-YOURSELF WORKBOOK FOR CANADIANS

Second Edition

Graham & Shirley Edis

McGraw-Hill Ryerson Limited
Toronto Montreal

**Trace Your Family Tree: a do-it-yourself workbook for Canadians**
**Second Edition**



ISBN 0-07-551463-X

1 2 3 4 5 6 7 8 9 0 AP 1 0 9 8 7 6 5 4 3 2

**Canadian Cataloguing in Publication Data**

Edis, Graham, 1933–
Trace your family tree

2nd ed.
ISBN 0-07-551463-X

1. Genealogy – Handbooks, manuals, etc. 2. Canada – Genealogy – Handbooks, manuals, etc. I. Edis, Shirley, 1935– . II. Title.

CS16.E35 1992 929.1'072 C92-094447-7

Cover photo: Alain Choisnet/The Image Bank Canada

Cover design: Hania Fil

Printed and bound in Canada

You are about to embark on one of the most fascinating of pastimes. You will become something of an historian, certainly a logical and deductive thinker, and a person anxious to reveal the role played by previous generations in shaping the world of today.

As an amateur genealogist you will become a type of historical detective delving into facts and figures until a true picture of your ancestor emerges.

You are joining thousands who are taking part in what is said to be the world's third most popular hobby. Rapidly growing in popularity, genealogy is only exceeded in participants as a pastime by coin and stamp collecting.

Libraries, archives, genealogical societies and historical groups world-wide have experienced a tremendous demand recently for information for those searching out their family trees. In Canada, local genealogical societies are expanding and the Public Archives in Ottawa is handling an unprecedented number of requests, while in the U.S. the pastime has created such interest that the Boy Scouts of America has added basic genealogy to its list of merit badges and more than 1,500 scouts earn the award each month.

So, despite the fact that you are generally on your own in discovering your particular family tree there are many other researchers doing the same thing and consequently a growing number of specialized aids are being developed to make your search successful.

# WHY MAKE THE SEARCH?

Reasons for searching out a family tree vary considerably. They range from attempts to link up the family with a long lost inheritance, to discover family relationships with important historical figures, to prepare material for an authentic family history, or merely to fulfil the urge to discover something of the hundreds of forebears that have resulted in your family line and created the unique individual that you are today. Whatever the reason, a duke, a witch, a pirate and many, many ordinary folk are all possible participants in your family line.

# GETTING STARTED

Civil registrations of births, marriages and deaths started at different times in each Canadian province. For Ontario 1869 was the official starting point, while in British Columbia official registration commenced in 1872. There are earlier records in many provinces though, with some Quebec church records going back to 1621.

Civil registration records may generally be obtained by contacting: The Recorder, Division of Vital Statistics, Department of Health and Social Development, or, in some cases, The Registrar General, Department of Health in the provincial capital. (See the listing at the end of this section.)

For a Canadian-born searcher who knows little of the family background, this then is the starting point in tracing a family tree. A birth certificate yields the name of your parents, your mother's maiden name, the family residence at the time and often some additional helpful information.

The next step is to obtain a copy of your parents' marriage certificate, for this states their age at the time of marrying and the names of your two grandfathers.

You are now hot on the trail of your eight great-grandparents, 16 great, great grandparents and so on until the family line leaves Canada for some other area, generally Europe.

Armed with the birth and marriage certificates and additional information you have gleaned from the family Bible, old newspaper clippings and diaries, and the memories of relatives, you can now start completing the basic genealogical form—the Family Group Record (see figure 1).

# COMPLETING THE SHEET

If you are married, place your full name, not initials, on the line marked ''Husband'' or ''Wife''. Complete the necessary birth and marriage place and dates and add the names of your father and mother. The details of your spouse should be similarly completed.

Women should use their maiden surnames on genealogical forms as these will be the main family names they will be following.

The line ''Christened'' (Chr.) will not generally be used until a period prior to the keeping of civil records.

# FAMILY GROUP RECORD



(figure 1)

**HUSBAND** George Francis Brown — Occupation: Welder

| | | | |
|---|---|---|---|
| Born | 4 September 1933 | Place | Calgary, Alberta, Canada |
| Chr. | | Place | |
| Marr. | 2 July 1956 | Place | Vancouver, B.C. Canada |
| Died | | Place | |
| Bur. | | Place | |
| Father | Francis Brown | Mother | Martha Young |
| Other Wives | | | |

**WIFE** Estelle Harrison

| | | | |
|---|---|---|---|
| Born | 17 January 1935 | Place | Nelson, B.C. Canada |
| Chr. | | Place | |
| Died | | Place | |
| Bur. | | Place | |
| Father | David Harrison | Mother | Jane Simpson |
| Other Husbands | | | |

| | Children | Sex | When Born / When Died | Where Born / Where Died | Marriage Date & Place / To Whom |
|---|---|---|---|---|---|
| 1 | George Donald | M | 12 Dec 1957 | Vancouver, B.C. Can | |
| 2 | Martha Lois | F | 2 July 1959 | Vancouver, B.C. Can | |
| 3 | Frank Andrew | M | 8 Sept 1961 | Vancouver, B.C. Can | |
| 4 | | | | | |
| 5 | | | | | |
| 6 | | | | | |
| 7 | | | | | |
| 8 | | | | | |
| 9 | | | | | |
| 10 | | | | | |
| 11 | | | | | |
| 12 | | | | | |
| 13 | | | | | |
| 14 | | | | | |
| 15 | | | | | |

| Sources of Information | Other Marriages |
|---|---|
| Birth Certificates George D., Martha L., & Frank A. | |
| Birth Certificate George F. Brown & Estelle Harrison | |
| Marriage Cert. George F. Brown & Estelle Harrison | |

**ORDER OF DATA**

NAME: John Henry BROWN
PLACE: Bramley, Hampshire, England
DATE: 2 September, 1832

You should now add the names of your children, their sex, birth dates and other details. Throughout all sheets relating to the family tree, dates should be recorded as day, month and year, i.e., 5 July 1873.

With the completion of the columns for ''Information Sources'' and ''Other Marriages'' your first family group record should be ready.

The next step is to list yourself as a child on another Family Group Record sheet along with your brothers and sisters, with your parents heading the sheet. For the unmarried this is the first sheet. At this stage you may be able to also list your parents' father and mother. Complete a similar form for your husband or wife so that there are now three forms—one showing you as a married couple and two showing each of you as a child in your parent's family group. (figure 2).

Your family records may allow you to go one step further without too much additional research—the completion of two sheets where your parents are listed as children. This is the record of your grandparents and should show your father or mother along with their brothers and sisters (your uncles and aunts).

If the names and details of your great grandparents are known to you then your pedigree has already expanded at a rapid rate and it is time you were mapping your progress on your pedigree chart.

# CHARTING YOUR PEDIGREE

The Pedigree Chart is a concise guide to your family line and does not carry all the details of a Family Group Record. It is designed to show the continuing ancestral line for each family group with room for four generations on each chart.

As illustrated (figures 2a and 3), the researcher's full name (maiden name for women) is written into line 1 with (if married) the name of husband or wife below. Your father's name and details should be placed on line 2, while your mother's maiden name should appear on line 3. Your father's father (your grandfather) should now appear on line 4 and your father's mother (your grandmother) on line 5.

# FAMILY GROUP RECORD

(figure 2)



**HUSBAND** Francis Brown — Occupation: Farmer

| | | | |
|---|---|---|---|
| Born | 4 August 1904 | Place | Saskatoon, Saskatchewan, Canada |
| Chr. | | Place | |
| Marr. | 7 February 1932 | Place | Calgary, Alberta, Canada |
| Died | 26 May 1969 | Place | Saskatoon, Saskatchewan, Canada |
| Bur. | 28 May 1969 | Place | Saskatoon, Saskatchewan, Canada |
| Father | James Henry Brown | Mother | Lucy Mitten |
| Other Wives | Jean Crompton | | |

**WIFE** Martha Young

| | | | |
|---|---|---|---|
| Born | 25 November 1910 | Place | Liverpool, Lancs., England |
| Chr. | | Place | |
| Died | | Place | |
| Bur. | | Place | |
| Father | James Young | Mother | Susan Winters |
| Other Husbands | | | |

| | Children | Sex | When Born / When Died | Where Born / Where Died | Marriage Date & Place / To Whom |
|---|---|---|---|---|---|
| 1 | George Francis | M | 4 Sept 1933 | Calgary, Alta. | 2 July 1956 Vancouver<br>Estelle Harrison |
| 2 | William Roy | M | 17 Nov 1935<br>4 Jan 1936 | Calgary, Alta.<br>Calgary, Alta. | |
| 3 | Jane Lois | F | 13 Oct 1937 | Saskatoon, Sask. | 14 Aug 1956 Saskatoon |
| 4 | Roger Donald | M | 4 Dec 1938 | Saskatoon, Sask. | |
| 5 | William | M | 10 July 1940 | Saskatoon, Sask. | |
| 6 | | | | | |
| 7 | | | | | |
| 8 | | | | | |
| 9 | | | | | |
| 10 | | | | | |
| 11 | | | | | |
| 12 | | | | | |
| 13 | | | | | |
| 14 | | | | | |
| 15 | | | | | |

| Sources of Information | Other Marriages |
|---|---|
| Family Bible in possession of Martha (Young) Brown | Jean Crompton -- |
| Birth Certificates George F., William R., Jane L., | 14 March 1925 at |
| Roger D. and William Brown | Saskatoon, Sask. |
| Death Certificate of Francis Brown | |
| Marriage Record of Francis Brown & Martha Young | |

**ORDER OF DATA**

NAME: John Henry BROWN
PLACE: Bramley, Hampshire, England
DATE: 2 September, 1832

Similarly your mother's parents will be placed on the lower lines. Her father should appear on line 6 and her mother (listing her maiden name) on line 7. Your Pedigree Chart has now been completed for three generations.

Now the fourth generation (your great grand-parents) can be added to the remainder of the chart. The basic rule to remember is that the male line takes the top lines 8, 10, 12 and 14, while the female ancestors take the lower lines 9, 11, 13 and 15 and are listed under their maiden names.

The Pedigree Chart is now complete for a single person or one member of a married couple. A similar Pedigree Chart should be completed for the husband or wife. Both husband and wife of a family tree research team can appear on the same Pedigree Chart if one of their children is used as the first generation on line 1. However, for simplicity, it is often preferable to keep separate charts for each side of the family.

Provision is made on each chart for index numbers so that the ancestral line may be continued accurately from a four generation pedigree chart to another, i.e., your great grandfather listed on line 8 of the chart number 1 will be re-listed on line 1 of a later pedigree chart with the index notation stating the person on line 1 is the same person as number 8 on chart number 1 (see figure 4). In this way you can add to a particular line of your pedigree whenever the information is available, whether it be next week or next year. It is not uncommon for a well researched pedigree to extend into twenty or thirty charts.

## SOLVING PROBLEMS

It may be that you have struck a problem or two in discovering some of the necessary details, then it is time to write a few letters (see samples figure 5).

Relatives, especially the older ones who may have access to records, should be contacted, residents and former neighbours in the old home town may be able to help. A well-written letter to the editor of a small town newspaper can sometimes start local amateur historians researching for you. Writing to similar family names found in directories can also be useful. A visit to the cemetary of the one-time family home town may also reveal important data on long forgotten stones.

# PEDIGREE CHART

(figure 2a)

CHART NO. ______

NO. 1 ON THIS CHART IS

THE SAME PERSON AS NO. ______

ON CHART NO. ______

1 YOUR NAME
BORN
WHERE
MARRIED
WHERE
DIED
WHERE

HUSBAND OR WIFE (if applicable)
NAME OF HUSBAND OR WIFE

2 YOUR FATHER
BORN
WHERE
MARRIED
WHERE
DIED
WHERE

3 YOUR MOTHER
BORN
WHERE
DIED
WHERE

4 YOUR FATHER'S FATHER
BORN (your grandfather)
WHERE
MARRIED
WHERE
DIED
WHERE

5 YOUR FATHER'S MOTHER
BORN (your grandmother)
WHERE
DIED
WHERE

6 YOUR MOTHER'S FATHER
BORN (your grandfather)
WHERE
MARRIED
WHERE
DIED
WHERE

7 YOUR MOTHER'S MOTHER
BORN (your grandmother)
WHERE
DIED
WHERE

8 YOUR GREAT GRANDFATHER
BORN
WHERE
MARRIED
WHERE
DIED
WHERE

9 YOUR GREAT GRANDMOTHER
BORN
WHERE
DIED
WHERE

10 YOUR GREAT GRANDFATHER
BORN
WHERE
MARRIED
WHERE
DIED
WHERE

11 YOUR GREAT GRANDMOTHER
BORN
WHERE
DIED
WHERE

12 YOUR GREAT GRANDFATHER
BORN
WHERE
MARRIED
WHERE
DIED
WHERE

13 YOUR GREAT GRANDMOTHER
BORN
WHERE
DIED
WHERE

14 YOUR GREAT GRANDFATHER
BORN
WHERE
MARRIED
WHERE
DIED
WHERE

15 YOUR GREAT GRANDMOTHER
BORN
WHERE
DIED
WHERE

**ORDER OF DATA**

NAME: John Henry BROWN
PLACE: Bramley, Hampshire, England
DATE: 2 September, 1832

# PEDIGREE CHART

(figure 3)

CHART NO. 1

NO. 1 ON THIS CHART IS
THE SAME PERSON AS NO. ______
ON CHART NO. ______

**1** George Francis Brown
BORN 4 September 1933
WHERE Calgary, Alta. Canada
MARRIED 2 July 1956
WHERE Vancouver, B.C.
DIED
WHERE

Estelle Harrison
NAME OF HUSBAND OR WIFE

**2** Francis Brown
BORN 4 August 1904
WHERE Saskatoon, Sask.
MARRIED 7 February 1932
WHERE Calgary, Alta.
DIED 26 May 1969
WHERE Saskatoon, Sask.

**3** Martha Young
BORN 25 November 1910
WHERE Liverpool Lancs. Eng.
DIED
WHERE

**4** James Henry Brown
BORN 29 May 1868
WHERE London, England
MARRIED 5 March 1895
WHERE Saskatoon, Sask.
DIED 30 April 1938
WHERE Saskatoon, Sask.

**5** Lucy Mitten
BORN 4 May 1873
WHERE Saskatoon, Sask.
DIED 5 October 1944
WHERE Saskatoon, Sask.

**6** James Young
BORN 17 June 1867
WHERE Liverpool Lancs.
MARRIED 6 November 1886
WHERE Liverpool Lancs.
DIED 8 January 1950
WHERE Calgary, Alta.

**7** Susan Winters
BORN 3 January 1869
WHERE Perranzabulae Crnwl
DIED 3 November 1949
WHERE Liverpool, Lancs.

**8** Henry Brown
BORN 7 October 1837
WHERE Wisbech Cambs. Eng. 2
MARRIED 3 June 1862
WHERE Wisbech, Cambs.
DIED 27 February 1904
WHERE Wisbech, Cambs.

**9** Jane Mason
BORN 19 August 1837
WHERE Gedney Hill Lincs 3
DIED 27 July 1890
WHERE Wisbech, Cambs.

**10** Eli Mitten
BORN 12 June 1848
WHERE Walton, Somerset 4
MARRIED 17 May 1870
WHERE Walton, Somerset
DIED 19 July 1925
WHERE Saskatoon, Sask.

**11** Sara Halstead
BORN 4 May 1853
WHERE Walton, Somerset 5
DIED 25 February 1876
WHERE Saskatoon, Sask.

**12** William Young
BORN 12 August 1844
WHERE Liverpool Lancs. 6
MARRIED 9 January 1867
WHERE Liverpool, Eng.
DIED 7 March 1900
WHERE Liverpool, Lancs.

**13** Martha Sutton
BORN 15 May 1848
WHERE Prescot, Lancs. 7
DIED 19 June 1867
WHERE Liverpool, Lancs.

**14** Robert Winters
BORN 22 April 1843
WHERE Perranzabulae Crn. 8
MARRIED 6 October 1866
WHERE St. Ives, Cornwall
DIED 23 December 1907
WHERE St. Ives, Cornwall

**15** Nancy Perry
BORN 20 December 1841
WHERE Towednack, Cornwl. 9
DIED 6 March 1908
WHERE St. Ives, Cornwall

**ORDER OF DATA**
NAME: John Henry BROWN
PLACE: Bramley, Hampshire, England
DATE: 2 September, 1832

If you have access to a library equipped with microfilm readers, copies of early Canadian newspapers can be examined for advertisements and obituaries. Any local library possessing microfilm readers and participating in the interlibrary loan arrangement can also make available to you much of the holdings of the Public Archives of Canada.

Census records for many provinces for the years 1851, 1861 and 1871 can greatly assist in finding a complete family unit if a former place of residence is known and a time period estimated. Land records and county atlases also exist for many provinces and can be used to discover early family locations.

# AVOIDING DUPLICATION

Duplication of effort is a common problem with many beginning genealogists. Unless an accurate recording is kept of the various steps taken to discover forebears, somewhere, sometime in the future, some of the work will be done again.

Professional genealogists use various types of systems to ensure each step in tracing a family line is recorded along with the results achieved.

Three forms have been developed to assist the beginning genealogist to set up an easy, efficient record keeping system which serves not only to record moves already made, but those planned for the future.

The Correspondence Log (figure 6) provides space for all necessary data when writing away for genealogical information. One page is provided for each family line, i.e., one page for the ''Young'' family research, another for letters concerning the ''Brown'' family, etc. A column is provided for a brief summary of results and another for reference numbers which may be used both for recording an index number on any certificate, letter or official document received, and for indexing pages of a note book or diary recording greater details of the search.

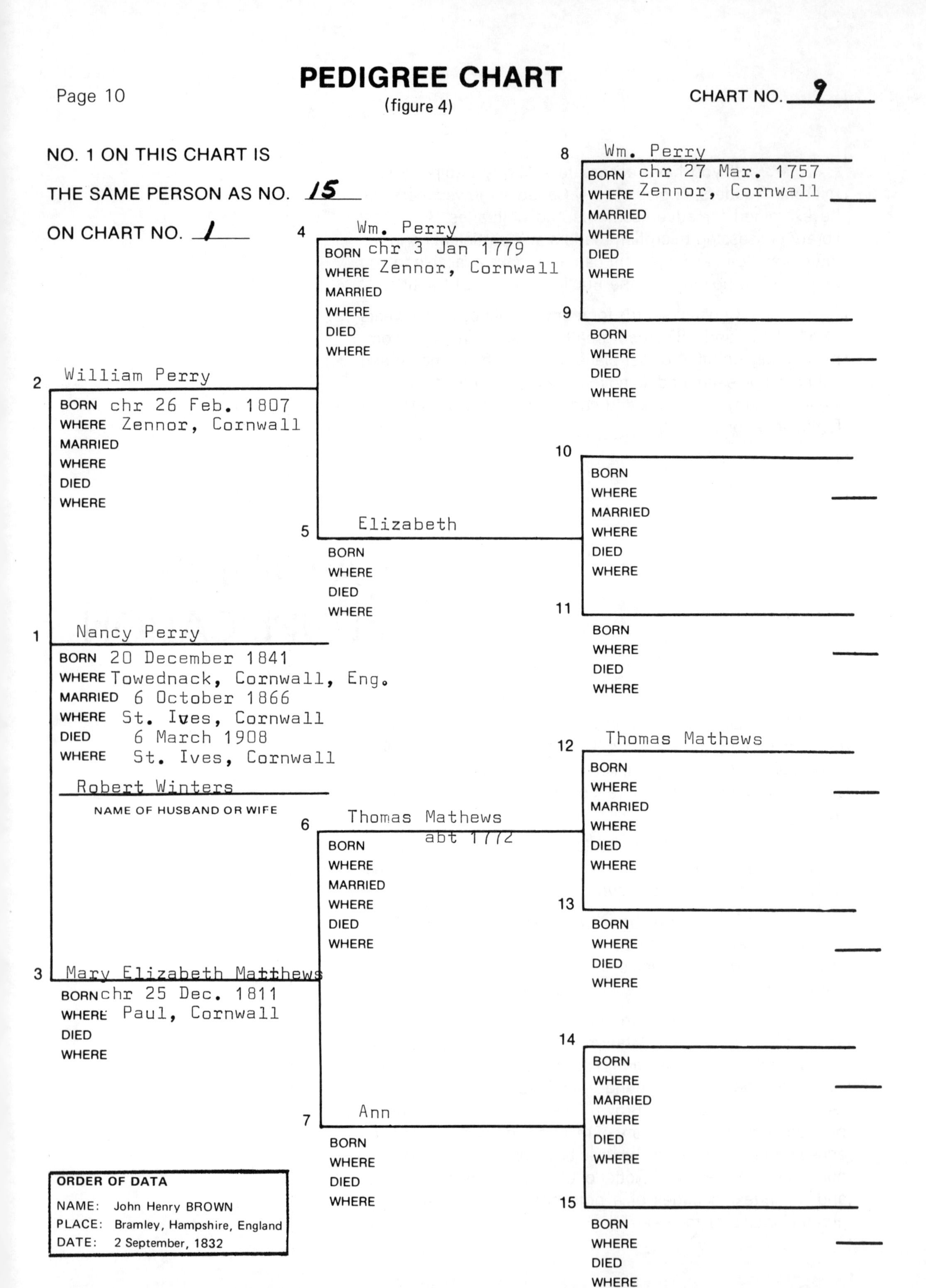

# PEDIGREE CHART

(figure 4)

CHART NO. 9

NO. 1 ON THIS CHART IS
THE SAME PERSON AS NO. 15
ON CHART NO. 1

8 Wm. Perry
BORN chr 27 Mar. 1757
WHERE Zennor, Cornwall
MARRIED
WHERE
DIED
WHERE

4 Wm. Perry
BORN chr 3 Jan 1779
WHERE Zennor, Cornwall
MARRIED
WHERE
DIED
WHERE

9
BORN
WHERE
DIED
WHERE

2 William Perry
BORN chr 26 Feb. 1807
WHERE Zennor, Cornwall
MARRIED
WHERE
DIED
WHERE

10
BORN
WHERE
MARRIED
WHERE
DIED
WHERE

5 Elizabeth
BORN
WHERE
DIED
WHERE

11
BORN
WHERE
DIED
WHERE

1 Nancy Perry
BORN 20 December 1841
WHERE Towednack, Cornwall, Eng.
MARRIED 6 October 1866
WHERE St. Ives, Cornwall
DIED 6 March 1908
WHERE St. Ives, Cornwall

Robert Winters
NAME OF HUSBAND OR WIFE

12 Thomas Mathews
BORN
WHERE
MARRIED
WHERE
DIED
WHERE

6 Thomas Mathews
abt 1772
BORN
WHERE
MARRIED
WHERE
DIED
WHERE

13
BORN
WHERE
DIED
WHERE

3 Mary Elizabeth Matthews
BORN chr 25 Dec. 1811
WHERE Paul, Cornwall
DIED
WHERE

14
BORN
WHERE
MARRIED
WHERE
DIED
WHERE

7 Ann
BORN
WHERE
DIED
WHERE

15
BORN
WHERE
DIED
WHERE

**ORDER OF DATA**

NAME: John Henry BROWN
PLACE: Bramley, Hampshire, England
DATE: 2 September, 1832

## SAMPLE LETTERS

(figure 5)

Date
Director,
Department of Vital Records (or) County Recorders Office
(or) Registry Office
Address
City, Province, State or Country

your address

Dear Sir:

I am interested in locating and obtaining a copy of the
(birth, marriage or death) record of ..........................................
who was my .............. (state relationship).

These are the facts I have. (Briefly give the necessary
details to establish identity)

If you will advise the fee for a search of your records
and a copy of the document, I will forward my money order,
(in pounds Sterling, in U.S. funds etc.)
(or)
Enclosed is the fee for the above requested search and
document.

Thank you for your assistance.

Sincerely,

Your name

***********

Date
The Rector,
Name of Church
Address
Town, Province, County, Country

Your address

Dear Sir:

After many months of research I now believe members of my
family were at one time members of your parish.

The following individuals may perhaps appear in your Parish
Register: ................................ (state names and
approximate dates).

I am most anxious to obtain the information pertaining to
my family and if you will advise the fee for a search of
your Register and for a copy of the information found, I
will forward my money order (in pounds Sterling etc.)

Thank you for your time and consideration.

Sincerely,

Your name

The log may also be used for forward planning by writing in ahead the project to be accomplished when time permits, such as: ''Oliver Journal'' letter to the editor re one-time resident John Brown or, ''Maude Hendry'' (Aunt Maude) re the lost family Bible.

The General Research Log takes over where the Correspondence Log leaves off, for it has special columns for recording book and document titles, call numbers and place of search. In addition to books and documents the General Research Log is ideally suited for an information summary of cemetary searches, memorials, land titles, wills, etc. It can be used for the same forward planning as the Correspondence Log, a project which saves much wasted effort later in the search.

While the general format of the right-hand side columns of the three logs is the same, each has been designed for its special individual use. The Microfilm Research log provides space for the titles of microfilms of genealogical records. Along with the date of order, loan source and film call number, the form has space for the loan period and date searched.

In all three logs it is essential to complete the results column recording if nothing was discovered or the family found and further recorded in the research diary.

## SEARCHING OUTSIDE CANADA

Outside Canada the task of letter writing takes on a greater importance unless you plan to visit the former homeland of your forebears.

If your ancestors were from Great Britain, and a large proportion of Canadians have British ancestry, you will need to search the Civil Records of St. Catherine's House, London, England. The civil recording of births, marriages and deaths in England and Wales started on July 1, 1837. Prior to this period the registers of Baptism, Marriages and Burials were kept in the parish churches throughout the

## CORRESPONDENCE LOG BROWN

FAMILY LINE

(figure 6)

| Date sent / Money | Follow up | Answer received / Refund | ADDRESSEE | SEARCHING FOR | RESULTS | Ref. No. |
|---|---|---|---|---|---|---|
| 18/3/72 | | 5/4/72 | Mrs. MaudeHendry | Family Bible | suggests Martha | 41 |
| | | | Vancouver, B.C. | | Brown has it | |
| 9/4/72 | | 28/4/72 | Martha Brown | Family Bible | Has it & copying | 42 |
| | | | Saskatoon Sask. | | family details | A2 |
| 7/6/72 | 4/8/72 | 10/11/72 | Vicar, Wisbech | Birth Henry abt | Chr. record & | 47 |
| $5.00 | | | Cambs. England | 1836 | parents | A2 |
| 7/6/72 | | | Editor "Sounder" | Info on Browns | published | 48 |
| | | | Saskatoon | in area | 20/6/72 letters | |

## GENERAL RESEARCH LOG YOUNG

FAMILY LINE

| Place of search | RECORD TITLE OR SOURCE | Call No. | SEARCHING FOR | Date searched | RESULTS | Ref. No. |
|---|---|---|---|---|---|---|
| Branch Gen. | Liverpool, England | | Young family | | Some Youngs | |
| Library | Directory 1842 | ENG 43 | (coach maker) | 14/4/72 | listed | A2 |
| Van. Pub. | Liverpool City Map | | area of residence | | Located Street & | |
| Library | & gazeteer | | of Youngs | 20/4/72 | district for 1851 census | A3 |
| Gen. Society | Liverpool newspaper | | Possible microfilmed | | | |
| Library | lists | | paper | | | |

## MICROFILM RESEARCH LOG PERRY

FAMILY LINE

| Date ordered / Loan source | FILM TITLE | Call No. | Loan period From: To: | SEARCHING FOR | Date searched | RESULTS | Ref. No. |
|---|---|---|---|---|---|---|---|
| 4/2/73 | Index to Civil Registration | | 26/3/73 | NANCY (ANNIE) | | not listed | |
| B.C. LIB | Births 1841 4th ¼ | 522,562 | 8/4/73 | PERRY | 26/3/73 | | |
| 14/4/73 | TOWEDNACK, CORNWALL | | 8/6/73 | Nancy Perry & | | not listed | |
| B.C. LIB | 1841 Census | 241,266 | 22/6/73 | family | 13/6/73 | | A 21 |
| 14/4/73 | VITAL RECORDS ZENNOR | | 14/6/73 | Births & Marriages | | Recorded Perrys | |
| B.C. LIB. | CORNWALL 1599-1837 | 254,221 | 28/6/73 | ~~Perry~~ fam. | 25/6/73 | but not Nancy | A22-24 |
| | Index to Civil Reg. Births | | | Nancy Perry - | | | |
| B.C. LIB. | 1842 1st quarter | | | birth | | | |
| | | | | | | | |
| | | | | | | | |

country. Many are still retained in the original church and the custodian, normally the local minister, is entitled to a fee for searching the ancient records.

While obtaining certificates from St. Catherine's House, London, is expensive and requires a great deal of initial information to locate the exact record, the pre-1837 parish registers can often be checked in Canada and U.S.A. at one of the branch libraries of the Genealogical Society of The Church of Jesus Christ of Latter-Day Saints. Located at Salt Lake City, Utah, the Genealogical Society is the largest repository of genealogical microfilm records in the world and much of its holdings are available at its branch libraries for its members and the general public. The branch libraries in Canada, however, are limited in number and usually located near the areas of greatest population in each province. These specialized libraries are listed later in this section.

Pre-1837 marriage licences and early wills are important sources for the genealogist. Census records for England and Wales, particularly for the years 1841, 1851, 1861 and 1871 are invaluable in locating ancestry where little else but a possible place of residence is known. These English census records also may be obtained through the local branch of the LDS Genealogical Society for a nominal loan fee, and checked in the library,

Research in other countries of the world requires a knowledge of record sources and periods and the current repositories—far too much information to be covered in this brief introductory section. Local libraries, provincial or district genealogical societies and the LDS branch libraries all have varying quantities of information available for the researcher. A list of books dealing with research in various areas is provided at the end of this section.

# MAKING MONEY FROM GENEALOGY

While the majority of genealogical researchers engage in the pastime to merely discover their origins, there are those whose main aim is to connect themselves with established lines of notable people. Although the fact that they are distantly related is sufficient for some there are others who pursue the search to establish claims on family fortunes and positions.

Although it is a lengthy and difficult task to establish recognizable and legal title to long unclaimed family fortunes, there is a growing number of individuals who make it a profession to trace rightful heirs to large estates and receive sizable percentages of them for making the heirs aware of their inheritances. With a number of estates of $100,000 or so going begging each year in Canada, the work of this type of researcher, the forensic genealogist, is growing.

Other professional genealogists who gain an income in a regular, if unspectacular manner, are primarily concerned with assisting, at an hourly fee, the amateur searcher or those too busy to attempt the task themselves. Usually accredited with one major genealogical society or another the professional in this field is a specialist in certain countries and has gained skills through years of successful research. The names of accredited researchers can usually be obtained from local Genealogical Societies or Branch Genealogical Libraries.

# FURTHER INFORMATION

The various books listed, and others you find in local libraries, could be the tools needed to give you the extended study you need to professionalize your research. Study with your own or borrowed books coupled with actual research is the most effective way to increase your research skills. However, membership of a Genealogical Society (see list) can also assist you to learn the craft quickly.

It is not really easy this business of tracing a family tree. Ancestors can be very elusive, tripping the researchers by naming a child after a brother who died in infancy, changing the spelling of the family surname and sometimes completely disappearing from record for a time. However, learning of the life and times of early ancestors can make the search very rewarding.

The fantastic scope of the search for ancestors and the gaining of formerly unknown relatives in all walks of life becomes evident when one works out the statistics of even a single family. Progressive doubling up from the family of today gives two parents, four grandparents, eight great grandparents, 16 great, great grandparents and so on.

Simple arithmetic reveals a possible million forebears in a mere 20 generations—plenty of room for a pirate or two, an earl or even a duke.

**Where to search first:**

*Talk with:*

Old family friends, family doctor, family lawyer, former neighbours, cousins, uncles, aunts, grandparents, etc.

*Search for:*

Old letters, family Bible inscriptions, old certificates, military service records, citizenship papers, legal documents such as wills, mortgages, insurance policies, old passports, etc.

*Locate also:*

Occupational records such as union registration, apprenticeship papers, membership documents for professional associations, etc.

*Check records of:*

Churches, youth groups, schools, fraternal bodies, service organizations, etc.

*Look for:*

Old photographs, scrapbooks, diaries and journals, newspaper clippings, address and birthday books, memorial cards, etc.

*Search also for:*

Family histories, biographies, existing genealogical records, etc.

**Major Canadian Genealogical Societies**

Vancouver: Genealogical Society of British Columbia, P.O. Box 94371, Richmond, British Columbia V6Y 2A8

Toronto: Ontario Genealogical Society, Box 66, Station Q, Toronto, Ontario M4T 2L7

Ottawa: Ontario Genealogical Society, P.O. Box 8346, Ottawa, Ontario K1G 3H8

Edmonton: Genealogical Society of Alberta, P.O. Box 3151, Station A, Edmonton, Alberta

Regina: Genealogical Society of Saskatchewan, P.O. Box 1894, Regina, Saskatchewan S4P 3E1

Montreal: Genealogical Society of Quebec, 335 Place D'Armes, Montreal, Quebec H2Y 3H1

## Canadian Civil Registrations

Although some vital statistics were recorded as far back as 1621 most civil registrations in Canada commenced in the late 19th century. The amount of information varies according to the period, but the following data is generally given:

*Births:*
Name, date and place of birth, parents' names, ages, residence and occupation.

*Deaths:*
Name, date and place of birth, date and place of death, occupation name and residence of deceased, date and place of burial, cause of death, parents' names, places of birth.

*Marriages:*
Names, date and place of marriage, sometimes ages, witnesses, person who performed ceremony, names of parents, residence of couple.

**Vital Statistics starting dates:**

| | |
|---|---|
| Alberta: | Complete records from 1898. Some births from 1853 and deaths from 1893. |
| British Columbia: | Official registration from 1872 but serious gaps in early years. |
| Manitoba: | Complete records from 1882. |
| New Brunswick: | Complete records exist from 1888 with some earlier births also listed. |
| Newfoundland: | Civil registration commenced in 1892. |
| Nova Scotia: | Although civil registration began in 1864, only marriages were recorded for the period 1876-1908. |
| Ontario: | 1 July 1869 was the starting date. |
| Prince Edward Island: | Civil records officially date from 1906. Some marriage records from 1783. |
| Quebec: | Civil registration complete from 1926. Church records go back to 1621. |
| Saskatchewan: | Incomplete records from 1878. Complete records from 1920. |
| Yukon: | Some births recorded from 1895 but complete records began in 1898. |
| Northwest Territories: | Few records exist prior to 1927. |

**Where to write for Vital Statistics:**

CANADA

| | |
|---|---|
| Alberta: | Division of Vital Statistics, Texaco Building, 10130 – 112th Street, Edmonton T5K 2K4 |
| British Columbia: | Division of Vital Statistics, 818 Fort Street, Victoria V8W 1H8 |
| Manitoba: | Division of Vital Statistics, Dept. of Health, 401 York Avenue, Winnipeg R3C 0P8 |
| New Brunswick: | Registrar General of Vital Statistics, Centennial Building, Box 6000, Fredericton E3B 5H1 |
| Newfoundland: | Division of Vital Statistics, Dept. of Health, P.O. Box 8700, St. Johns A1B 4J6 |
| Nova Scotia: | Division of Vital Statistics, Dept. of Health, Provincial Building, Box 157, Halifax B3J 2M9 |
| Ontario: | Office of the Registrar General, Macdonald Block, Queen's Park, Toronto M7A 1Y5 |
| Prince Edward Island: | Director of Vital Statistics, Dept. of Health, Box 2000, Charlottetown C1A 7N8 |
| Quebec: | Population Registrar, Dept. of Social Affairs, 1279 Boul. Charest Ouest, (3c), Quebec G1N 2C9 |
| Saskatchewan: | Director of Vital Statistics, Dept. of Public Health, 3475 Albert Street, Regina S4S 6X6 |
| Yukon: | Dept. of Territorial Secretary & Registrar General, Box 2703, Whitehorse Y1A 2C6 |
| Northwest Territories: | Registrar General of Vital Statistics, P.O. Box 1320, Yellowknife X0E 1N0 |
| **ENGLAND** | General Register Office, Postal Applications, Room 9, Smedley Hydro, Trafalgar Road, Southport, Merseyside England PR8 2HH |
| **SCOTLAND** | General Register Office, New Register House, Edinburgh, Scotland EH1 3YT |
| **IRELAND** | Registrar General's Office, Custom House, Dublin |

| | |
|---|---|
| ULSTER | General Register Office, Oxford House, 49–55 Chichester Street, Belfast, Ireland BT1 4HL |
| U.S.A. | County Recorder, (County Seat of the County where you are searching) State, Zip Code |
| AUSTRIA | Direktor, Staatsarchiv, Minoritenplatz 1, 1010 Vienna, Austria (This office may assist in determining the town holding the records.) |
| BELGIUM | General Archives, (Archives Generales du Royaume), 78 Galerie Ravenstein, Brussels, Belgium |
| DENMARK | Public Record Office, Rigsarkivet, Copenhagen, Denmark |
| FRANCE | Ministere de l'Education Nationale: Direction des Archives de France, 110 Rue de Grenelle 75357, Paris, France |
| GERMANY | Chief Registry Office, Hauptstandesmt Hamburg, Johanniswal 14, Hamburg 1, Germany (To determine town holding records for your area.) Or write directly to the Registrar, Standesamt, of the town in question. |
| ITALY | Each town holds its own records in the civil registry office, the Ufficio de Stato Civile. To determine who holds the records for your area write to Istituto Centrale de Statistica, via Cesare Balbo 16, Rome, Italy. |
| NETHERLANDS | Central Archive, Algemeen Riksarchief, Bleijenburg, The Hague, Netherlands |
| NORWAY | Central Bureau of Statistics, The Demographic Section, Statistik Sentrablyra, Dronningens Gate 16, Oslo, Norway |
| SPAIN | Secretary, Instituto Internacional de Genealogia y Heraldica, Apartado de Correos, 12,079, Madrid, Spain |
| SWEDEN | Central Bureau of Statistics, Statitiska Centralbyrans Arkiv, Linnegatan 87, Stockholm O, Sweden |
| SWITZERLAND | Records are held in each province, called a canton. Locate the capital of the canton in which you are searching. Address your inquiry to the Director, Canton Archives, (Town name), (Canton name), Switzerland |

**Canadian Census Records**

Canadian population records are valuable sources of family records. Although not all have been preserved, those listed are generally available from the Public Archives, Ottawa, or any library equipped with microfilm readers and operating an inter-library loan system with the Public Archives of Canada.

Acadia: 1671, 1686, 1693, 1698, 1701 and 1714 census return enumerate every person.

1703, 1707 and 1739 censuses indicate heads of families only and provide some details of family size.

1730, 1734 and 1735 returns (heads of families) are recorded for Ile St. Jean only. 1734 and 1753 (HF), 1749-1750 (all persons) are microfilmed for Ile Royale. 1741 Louisbourg census lists landholders only. 1717 and 1722 records for Port Toulouse lists heads of families, while the 1717 and 1719 census of Port Dauphin lists principal settlers only. 1739 census of Riviere S. Jean records the heads of families and 1761 enumeration of Gaspe to Baie Verte (incomplete) covers inhabitants generally.

Manitoba: 1832, 1834, 1835, 1840, 1843, 1846 and 1849 enumeration lists heads of families with some details of size of family and occupation. 1870 census lists each individual, age, sex, country or province of birth, religion, occupation, racial origin, marital status, etc. 1856 census is incomplete and has not been microfilmed.

New Brunswick: 1851, 1861 and 1871 census returns list each individual along with age, sex, country or province of birth, religion, racial origin, occupation, marital status, etc.

Newfoundland: 1691 and 1693 returns list each individual and some information regarding age, sex, country of birth, etc. 1704 census lists heads of families only.

Census records for Plaisance only are available for the years 1671, 1673 (all persons), 1698, 1706 and 1711 (HF).

Nova Scotia: 1770, 1773, 1775, and 1787 returns list heads of families only (not microfilmed); are located in the Nova Scotia Archives.

1817 (incomplete), 1827, 1838 and 1861 censuses list heads of families only. 1871 lists all persons. On microfilm also are Cape Breton returns, 1811 and 1818; City of Halifax, Halifax County and King's County, 1851; City of Halifax only, 1858.

Before 1770 refer to Acadian census records.

| | |
|---|---|
| Ontario: | 1842, 1848 and 1850 returns list heads of families only. 1848 and 1850 records are incomplete.<br><br>1851, 1861 and 1871 returns enumerate complete families with some information concerning age, country of birth, religion, occupation, marital status and racial origin.<br><br>1796, 1806, 1813, 1823 and 1824 censuses for Augusta Township (HF) are also on microfilm. |
| Prince Edward Island: | 1798 census (HF) has not been microfilmed but is published in Duncan Campbell's ''History of Prince Edward Island.''<br><br>1841 and 1861 returns list heads of families. |
| Quebec: | 1666, 1667, 1681, 1851, 1861 and 1871 returns cover complete families with varying information as to age, country of birth, religion, occupation, marital status, racial origin and education. 1825, 1831 and 1842 returns list heads of families only. |

Canadian census returns for 1881 also have recently been released for public use.

**Family History Centres of The Genealogical Society of the Church of Jesus Christ of Latter-Day Saints, Utah, U.S.A.**

(Usually in a portion of an L.D.S. church building.)

| | |
|---|---|
| Calgary | 2021 – 17th Avenue S.W., Calgary, Alberta |
| Cardston | 846 First Avenue W., Cardston, Alberta |
| Edmonton | 9010 – 85th Street, Edmonton, Alberta |
| Grande Prairie | 11212 – 102nd Street, Grande Prairie, Alberta |
| Lethbridge | 2808 – 28th Street S., Lethbridge, Alberta |
| Raymond | Second N 200 W, Raymond, Alberta |
| Red Deer | 3002 – 47th Avenue, Red Deer, Alberta |
| Spruce Grove | 400 McLeod Avenue, Edmonton, Alberta |
| Taber | 4709 – 50th Avenue, Taber, Alberta |
| Burnaby | 5280 Kincaid Street, Burnaby, B.C. |
| Courtenay | 1901 20th Street, Courtenay, B.C. |
| Cranbrook | 2210 Second Street N., Cranbrook, B.C. |
| Fort St. John | 11412 – 100th Street, Fort St. John, B.C. |
| Kamloops | 2165 Parkcrest Avenue, Kamloops, B.C. |
| Kelowna | Glenmore & Ivans Streets, Kelowna, B.C. |
| Prince George | 4180 Fifth Avenue, Prince George, B.C. |
| Terrace | 1744 Kenworth Street, Terrace, B.C. |
| Victoria | 701 Mann Avenue, Victoria, B.C. |
| Winnipeg | 45 Dalhousie Drive, Winnipeg, Manitoba |
| St. John | 177 Manchester Avenue, St. John, N.B. |
| Dartmouth | 44 Cumberland Drive, Dartmouth, Nova Scotia |
| Brampton | Wanless Drive, Brampton, Ontario |
| Chatham | 23 Detroit Drive, Chatham, Ontario |
| Etobicoke | 95 Melbert Street, Etobicoke, Ontario |
| Fort Frances | 700 Third Street W., Ft. Frances, Ontario |
| Glenburnie | Glenburnie & Battersea, Glenburnie, Ontario |
| Hamilton | 701 Stonechurch Road E., Hamilton, Ontario |
| Kitchener | 10 Lorraine Avenue, Kitchener, Ontario |
| London | 1139 Riverside Drive, London, Ontario |
| Oshawa | 632 Thornton Road N., Oshawa, Ontario |
| Ottawa | 1017 Prince of Wales Drive, Ottawa, Ontario |
| Sarnia | 1400 Murphy Road, Sarnia, Ontario |
| Sault Ste. Marie | 126 Caledon Street, Sault Ste. Marie, Ontario |
| St. Thomas | 436 Elm Street, St. Thomas, Ontario |
| Thunder Bay | 2255 Ponderosa Drive, Thunder Bay, Ontario |
| Timmins | 500 Toke Street, Timmins, Ontario |
| Windsor | 33500 Forest Geode Drive, Windsor, Ontario |
| Montreal | (English) 6666 Perrebonne St., Montreal, Que |
| | (French) 470 Guilford Street, Montreal, Que |
| Regina | 550 Sangster Boulevard, Regina, Saskatchewan |
| Saskatoon | 1427 Tenth Street E., Saskatoon, Saskatchewan |

**General Library Resources:**

Books and microfilm dealing with genealogical research are generally found in the 929 section of libraries using the Dewey catalog system, and in the CS section of libraries using the Library of Congress catalog system.

## RELATIONSHIP CHART

KEY TO USING THE RELATIONSHIP CHART

1. To determine the relationship of the brothers (or sisters) of direct ancestors, follow the horizon-line from the direct ancestor.

   EXAMPLES:

   a. The brother of your 6 GG FATHER is your 6 GG UNCLE. Your relationship to him is shown in brackets immediately below the uncle relationship, in this case (6 gg nephew).

   b. The sister of your 6 GG FATHER is your 6 GG AUNT.

2. To determine your relationship to the children of the brothers (or sisters) of your direct ancestors, follow the vertical line down from the uncle (or aunt) relationship.

   EXAMPLES:

   a. The son of your 4 GG UNCLE is your 1c5r.

   b. The grandson of your GG UNCLE is your 2c1r.

ABBREVIATIONS; G FATHER = grandfather; GG FATHER = great grandfather; UNC = uncle; COU = cousin; c = cousin; neph = nephew; r = generations removed.

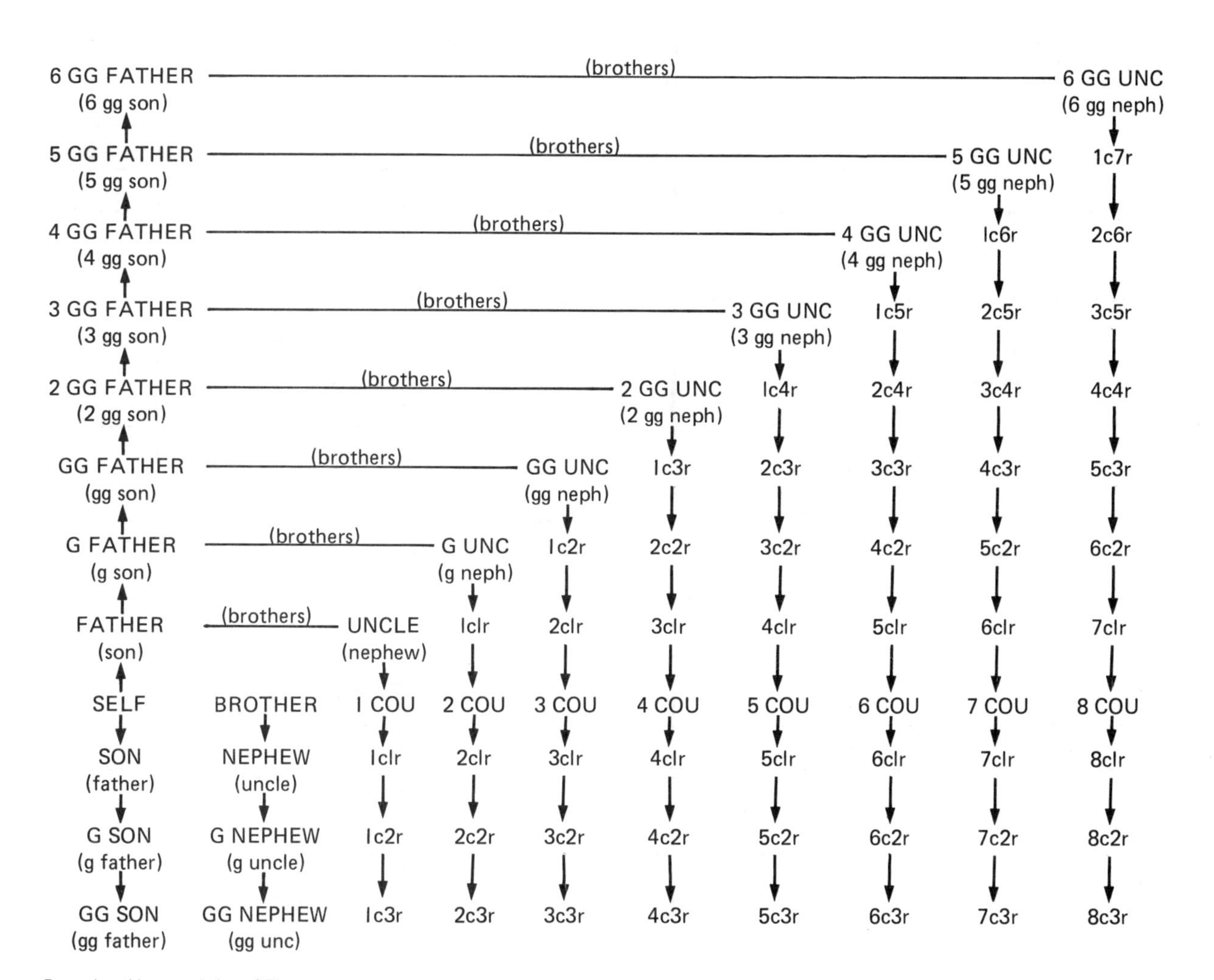

# CORRESPONDENCE LOG ______________________

FAMILY LINE

| Date sent / Money | Follow up | Answer received / Refund | ADDRESSEE | SEARCHING FOR | RESULTS | Ref. No. |
|---|---|---|---|---|---|---|
| | | | | | | |

# CORRESPONDENCE LOG

FAMILY LINE

| Date sent / Money | Follow up | Answer received / Refund | ADDRESSEE | SEARCHING FOR | RESULTS | Ref. No. |
|---|---|---|---|---|---|---|
| | | | | | | |
| | | | | | | |
| | | | | | | |
| | | | | | | |
| | | | | | | |
| | | | | | | |
| | | | | | | |
| | | | | | | |
| | | | | | | |
| | | | | | | |
| | | | | | | |
| | | | | | | |
| | | | | | | |
| | | | | | | |
| | | | | | | |
| | | | | | | |
| | | | | | | |
| | | | | | | |

# CORRESPONDENCE LOG ____________________
FAMILY LINE

| Date sent / Money | Follow up | Answer received / Refund | ADDRESSEE | SEARCHING FOR | RESULTS | Ref. No. |
|---|---|---|---|---|---|---|
| | | | | | | |
| | | | | | | |
| | | | | | | |
| | | | | | | |
| | | | | | | |
| | | | | | | |
| | | | | | | |
| | | | | | | |
| | | | | | | |
| | | | | | | |
| | | | | | | |
| | | | | | | |
| | | | | | | |
| | | | | | | |
| | | | | | | |
| | | | | | | |
| | | | | | | |
| | | | | | | |

# CORRESPONDENCE LOG ____________________

FAMILY LINE

| Date sent / Money | Follow up | Answer received / Refund | ADDRESSEE | SEARCHING FOR | RESULTS | Ref. No. |
|---|---|---|---|---|---|---|
| | | | | | | |
| | | | | | | |
| | | | | | | |
| | | | | | | |
| | | | | | | |
| | | | | | | |
| | | | | | | |
| | | | | | | |
| | | | | | | |
| | | | | | | |
| | | | | | | |
| | | | | | | |
| | | | | | | |
| | | | | | | |
| | | | | | | |
| | | | | | | |
| | | | | | | |
| | | | | | | |

# CORRESPONDENCE LOG ____________________

FAMILY LINE

| Date sent / Money | Follow up | Answer received / Refund | ADDRESSEE | SEARCHING FOR | RESULTS | Ref. No. |
|---|---|---|---|---|---|---|
| | | | | | | |

# CORRESPONDENCE LOG ____________________

FAMILY LINE

| Date sent | Follow up | Answer received | ADDRESSEE | SEARCHING FOR | RESULTS | Ref. No. |
|---|---|---|---|---|---|---|
| Money | | Refund | | | | |

# CORRESPONDENCE LOG ____________________

FAMILY LINE

| Date sent / Money | Follow up | Answer received / Refund | ADDRESSEE | SEARCHING FOR | RESULTS | Ref. No. |
|---|---|---|---|---|---|---|
| | | | | | | |
| | | | | | | |
| | | | | | | |
| | | | | | | |
| | | | | | | |
| | | | | | | |
| | | | | | | |
| | | | | | | |
| | | | | | | |
| | | | | | | |
| | | | | | | |
| | | | | | | |
| | | | | | | |
| | | | | | | |
| | | | | | | |
| | | | | | | |
| | | | | | | |
| | | | | | | |

# CORRESPONDENCE LOG

______________________
FAMILY LINE

| Date sent / Money | Follow up | Answer received / Refund | ADDRESSEE | SEARCHING FOR | RESULTS | Ref. No. |
| --- | --- | --- | --- | --- | --- | --- |
| | | | | | | |
| | | | | | | |
| | | | | | | |
| | | | | | | |
| | | | | | | |
| | | | | | | |
| | | | | | | |
| | | | | | | |
| | | | | | | |
| | | | | | | |
| | | | | | | |
| | | | | | | |
| | | | | | | |
| | | | | | | |
| | | | | | | |
| | | | | | | |
| | | | | | | |
| | | | | | | |

# CORRESPONDENCE LOG ____________________

FAMILY LINE

| Date sent / Money | Follow up | Answer received / Refund | ADDRESSEE | SEARCHING FOR | RESULTS | Ref. No. |
|---|---|---|---|---|---|---|
| | | | | | | |

# CORRESPONDENCE LOG ____________________

FAMILY LINE

| Date sent / Money | Follow up | Answer received / Refund | ADDRESSEE | SEARCHING FOR | RESULTS | Ref. No. |
|---|---|---|---|---|---|---|
| | | | | | | |
| | | | | | | |
| | | | | | | |
| | | | | | | |
| | | | | | | |
| | | | | | | |
| | | | | | | |
| | | | | | | |
| | | | | | | |
| | | | | | | |
| | | | | | | |
| | | | | | | |
| | | | | | | |
| | | | | | | |
| | | | | | | |
| | | | | | | |
| | | | | | | |
| | | | | | | |

# CORRESPONDENCE LOG ____________________

FAMILY LINE

| Date sent / Money | Follow up | Answer received / Refund | ADDRESSEE | SEARCHING FOR | RESULTS | Ref. No. |
|---|---|---|---|---|---|---|
| | | | | | | |

# CORRESPONDENCE LOG

FAMILY LINE

| Date sent / Money | Follow up | Answer received / Refund | ADDRESSEE | SEARCHING FOR | RESULTS | Ref. No. |
|---|---|---|---|---|---|---|
| | | | | | | |
| | | | | | | |
| | | | | | | |
| | | | | | | |
| | | | | | | |
| | | | | | | |
| | | | | | | |
| | | | | | | |
| | | | | | | |
| | | | | | | |
| | | | | | | |
| | | | | | | |
| | | | | | | |
| | | | | | | |
| | | | | | | |
| | | | | | | |
| | | | | | | |
| | | | | | | |

# CORRESPONDENCE LOG ______________________

FAMILY LINE

| Date sent / Money | Follow up | Answer received / Refund | ADDRESSEE | SEARCHING FOR | RESULTS | Ref. No. |
|---|---|---|---|---|---|---|
| | | | | | | |
| | | | | | | |
| | | | | | | |
| | | | | | | |
| | | | | | | |
| | | | | | | |
| | | | | | | |
| | | | | | | |
| | | | | | | |
| | | | | | | |
| | | | | | | |
| | | | | | | |
| | | | | | | |
| | | | | | | |
| | | | | | | |
| | | | | | | |
| | | | | | | |
| | | | | | | |

# CORRESPONDENCE LOG ______________________

FAMILY LINE

| Date sent / Money | Follow up | Answer received / Refund | ADDRESSEE | SEARCHING FOR | RESULTS | Ref. No. |
|---|---|---|---|---|---|---|
| | | | | | | |

# CORRESPONDENCE LOG

FAMILY LINE ______________________

| Date sent / Money | Follow up | Answer received / Refund | ADDRESSEE | SEARCHING FOR | RESULTS | Ref. No. |
|---|---|---|---|---|---|---|
| | | | | | | |

# GENERAL RESEARCH LOG

FAMILY LINE

| Place of search | RECORD TITLE OR SOURCE | Call No. | SEARCHING FOR | Date searched | RESULTS | Ref. No. |
|---|---|---|---|---|---|---|
| | | | | | | |
| | | | | | | |
| | | | | | | |
| | | | | | | |
| | | | | | | |
| | | | | | | |
| | | | | | | |
| | | | | | | |
| | | | | | | |
| | | | | | | |
| | | | | | | |
| | | | | | | |
| | | | | | | |
| | | | | | | |
| | | | | | | |
| | | | | | | |
| | | | | | | |
| | | | | | | |

# GENERAL RESEARCH LOG ____________

FAMILY LINE

| Place of search | RECORD TITLE OR SOURCE | Call No. | SEARCHING FOR | Date searched | RESULTS | Ref. No. |
|---|---|---|---|---|---|---|
| | | | | | | |
| | | | | | | |
| | | | | | | |
| | | | | | | |
| | | | | | | |
| | | | | | | |
| | | | | | | |
| | | | | | | |
| | | | | | | |
| | | | | | | |
| | | | | | | |
| | | | | | | |
| | | | | | | |
| | | | | | | |
| | | | | | | |
| | | | | | | |
| | | | | | | |
| | | | | | | |

# GENERAL RESEARCH LOG ______________

FAMILY LINE

| Place of search | RECORD TITLE OR SOURCE | Call No. | SEARCHING FOR | Date searched | RESULTS | Ref. No. |
|---|---|---|---|---|---|---|
| | | | | | | |
| | | | | | | |
| | | | | | | |
| | | | | | | |
| | | | | | | |
| | | | | | | |
| | | | | | | |
| | | | | | | |
| | | | | | | |
| | | | | | | |
| | | | | | | |
| | | | | | | |
| | | | | | | |
| | | | | | | |
| | | | | | | |
| | | | | | | |
| | | | | | | |
| | | | | | | |

# GENERAL RESEARCH LOG ____________________

FAMILY LINE

| Place of search | RECORD TITLE OR SOURCE | Call No. | SEARCHING FOR | Date searched | RESULTS | Ref. No. |
|---|---|---|---|---|---|---|
| | | | | | | |

# GENERAL RESEARCH LOG ____________

FAMILY LINE

| Place of search | RECORD TITLE OR SOURCE | Call No. | SEARCHING FOR | Date searched | RESULTS | Ref. No. |
|---|---|---|---|---|---|---|
| | | | | | | |
| | | | | | | |
| | | | | | | |
| | | | | | | |
| | | | | | | |
| | | | | | | |
| | | | | | | |
| | | | | | | |
| | | | | | | |
| | | | | | | |
| | | | | | | |
| | | | | | | |
| | | | | | | |
| | | | | | | |
| | | | | | | |
| | | | | | | |
| | | | | | | |
| | | | | | | |

# GENERAL RESEARCH LOG ________________

FAMILY LINE

| Place of search | RECORD TITLE OR SOURCE | Call No. | SEARCHING FOR | Date searched | RESULTS | Ref. No. |
|---|---|---|---|---|---|---|
| | | | | | | |
| | | | | | | |
| | | | | | | |
| | | | | | | |
| | | | | | | |
| | | | | | | |
| | | | | | | |
| | | | | | | |
| | | | | | | |
| | | | | | | |
| | | | | | | |
| | | | | | | |
| | | | | | | |
| | | | | | | |
| | | | | | | |
| | | | | | | |
| | | | | | | |
| | | | | | | |

# GENERAL RESEARCH LOG ____________________

FAMILY LINE

| Place of search | RECORD TITLE OR SOURCE | Call No. | SEARCHING FOR | Date searched | RESULTS | Ref. No. |
|---|---|---|---|---|---|---|
| | | | | | | |
| | | | | | | |
| | | | | | | |
| | | | | | | |
| | | | | | | |
| | | | | | | |
| | | | | | | |
| | | | | | | |
| | | | | | | |
| | | | | | | |
| | | | | | | |
| | | | | | | |
| | | | | | | |
| | | | | | | |
| | | | | | | |
| | | | | | | |
| | | | | | | |
| | | | | | | |

# GENERAL RESEARCH LOG ______________

FAMILY LINE

| Place of search | RECORD TITLE OR SOURCE | Call No. | SEARCHING FOR | Date searched | RESULTS | Ref. No. |
|---|---|---|---|---|---|---|
| | | | | | | |
| | | | | | | |
| | | | | | | |
| | | | | | | |
| | | | | | | |
| | | | | | | |
| | | | | | | |
| | | | | | | |
| | | | | | | |
| | | | | | | |
| | | | | | | |
| | | | | | | |
| | | | | | | |
| | | | | | | |
| | | | | | | |
| | | | | | | |
| | | | | | | |
| | | | | | | |

# GENERAL RESEARCH LOG

FAMILY LINE

| Place of search | RECORD TITLE OR SOURCE | Call No. | SEARCHING FOR | Date searched | RESULTS | Ref. No. |
|---|---|---|---|---|---|---|
| | | | | | | |
| | | | | | | |
| | | | | | | |
| | | | | | | |
| | | | | | | |
| | | | | | | |
| | | | | | | |
| | | | | | | |
| | | | | | | |
| | | | | | | |
| | | | | | | |
| | | | | | | |
| | | | | | | |
| | | | | | | |
| | | | | | | |
| | | | | | | |
| | | | | | | |
| | | | | | | |

# GENERAL RESEARCH LOG ____________

FAMILY LINE

| Place of search | RECORD TITLE OR SOURCE | Call No. | SEARCHING FOR | Date searched | RESULTS | Ref. No. |
|---|---|---|---|---|---|---|
| | | | | | | |
| | | | | | | |
| | | | | | | |
| | | | | | | |
| | | | | | | |
| | | | | | | |
| | | | | | | |
| | | | | | | |
| | | | | | | |
| | | | | | | |
| | | | | | | |
| | | | | | | |
| | | | | | | |
| | | | | | | |
| | | | | | | |
| | | | | | | |
| | | | | | | |
| | | | | | | |

# GENERAL RESEARCH LOG ________________

FAMILY LINE

| Place of search | RECORD TITLE OR SOURCE | Call No. | SEARCHING FOR | Date searched | RESULTS | Ref. No. |
|---|---|---|---|---|---|---|
| | | | | | | |
| | | | | | | |
| | | | | | | |
| | | | | | | |
| | | | | | | |
| | | | | | | |
| | | | | | | |
| | | | | | | |
| | | | | | | |
| | | | | | | |
| | | | | | | |
| | | | | | | |
| | | | | | | |
| | | | | | | |
| | | | | | | |
| | | | | | | |
| | | | | | | |
| | | | | | | |

# GENERAL RESEARCH LOG ____________
FAMILY LINE

| Place of search | RECORD TITLE OR SOURCE | Call No. | SEARCHING FOR | Date searched | RESULTS | Ref. No. |
|---|---|---|---|---|---|---|
| | | | | | | |
| | | | | | | |
| | | | | | | |
| | | | | | | |
| | | | | | | |
| | | | | | | |
| | | | | | | |
| | | | | | | |
| | | | | | | |
| | | | | | | |
| | | | | | | |
| | | | | | | |
| | | | | | | |
| | | | | | | |
| | | | | | | |
| | | | | | | |
| | | | | | | |
| | | | | | | |

# GENERAL RESEARCH LOG

______________________
FAMILY LINE

| Place of search | RECORD TITLE OR SOURCE | Call No. | SEARCHING FOR | Date searched | RESULTS | Ref. No. |
|---|---|---|---|---|---|---|
| | | | | | | |
| | | | | | | |
| | | | | | | |
| | | | | | | |
| | | | | | | |
| | | | | | | |
| | | | | | | |
| | | | | | | |
| | | | | | | |
| | | | | | | |
| | | | | | | |
| | | | | | | |
| | | | | | | |
| | | | | | | |
| | | | | | | |
| | | | | | | |
| | | | | | | |
| | | | | | | |

# GENERAL RESEARCH LOG ______________
FAMILY LINE

| Place of search | RECORD TITLE OR SOURCE | Call No. | SEARCHING FOR | Date searched | RESULTS | Ref. No. |
| --- | --- | --- | --- | --- | --- | --- |
| | | | | | | |
| | | | | | | |
| | | | | | | |
| | | | | | | |
| | | | | | | |
| | | | | | | |
| | | | | | | |
| | | | | | | |
| | | | | | | |
| | | | | | | |
| | | | | | | |
| | | | | | | |
| | | | | | | |
| | | | | | | |
| | | | | | | |
| | | | | | | |
| | | | | | | |
| | | | | | | |

# GENERAL RESEARCH LOG

_______________
FAMILY LINE

| Place of search | RECORD TITLE OR SOURCE | Call No. | SEARCHING FOR | Date searched | RESULTS | Ref. No. |
|---|---|---|---|---|---|---|
| | | | | | | |
| | | | | | | |
| | | | | | | |
| | | | | | | |
| | | | | | | |
| | | | | | | |
| | | | | | | |
| | | | | | | |
| | | | | | | |
| | | | | | | |
| | | | | | | |
| | | | | | | |
| | | | | | | |
| | | | | | | |
| | | | | | | |
| | | | | | | |
| | | | | | | |
| | | | | | | |

# MICROFILM RESEARCH LOG

__________________
FAMILY LINE

| Date ordered / Loan source | FILM TITLE | Call No. | Loan period From: To: | SEARCHING FOR | Date searched | RESULTS | Ref. No. |
|---|---|---|---|---|---|---|---|
| | | | | | | | |
| | | | | | | | |
| | | | | | | | |
| | | | | | | | |
| | | | | | | | |
| | | | | | | | |
| | | | | | | | |
| | | | | | | | |
| | | | | | | | |
| | | | | | | | |
| | | | | | | | |
| | | | | | | | |
| | | | | | | | |
| | | | | | | | |
| | | | | | | | |
| | | | | | | | |
| | | | | | | | |
| | | | | | | | |

# MICROFILM RESEARCH LOG

FAMILY LINE

| Date ordered / Loan source | FILM TITLE / Call No. | Loan period From: To: | SEARCHING FOR / Date searched | RESULTS | Ref. No. |
|---|---|---|---|---|---|
| | | | | | |
| | | | | | |
| | | | | | |
| | | | | | |
| | | | | | |
| | | | | | |
| | | | | | |
| | | | | | |
| | | | | | |
| | | | | | |
| | | | | | |
| | | | | | |
| | | | | | |
| | | | | | |
| | | | | | |
| | | | | | |
| | | | | | |
| | | | | | |

# MICROFILM RESEARCH LOG

---------------------------
FAMILY LINE

| Date ordered / Loan source | FILM TITLE / Call No. | Loan period From: To: | SEARCHING FOR / Date searched | RESULTS | Ref. No. |
|---|---|---|---|---|---|
| | | | | | |
| | | | | | |
| | | | | | |
| | | | | | |
| | | | | | |
| | | | | | |
| | | | | | |
| | | | | | |
| | | | | | |
| | | | | | |
| | | | | | |
| | | | | | |
| | | | | | |
| | | | | | |
| | | | | | |
| | | | | | |
| | | | | | |
| | | | | | |

# MICROFILM RESEARCH LOG

______________________
FAMILY LINE

| Date ordered<br>Loan source | FILM TITLE | Call No. | Loan period<br>From:<br>To: | SEARCHING FOR | Date searched | RESULTS | Ref. No. |
| --- | --- | --- | --- | --- | --- | --- | --- |
| | | | | | | | |
| | | | | | | | |
| | | | | | | | |
| | | | | | | | |
| | | | | | | | |
| | | | | | | | |
| | | | | | | | |
| | | | | | | | |
| | | | | | | | |
| | | | | | | | |
| | | | | | | | |
| | | | | | | | |
| | | | | | | | |
| | | | | | | | |
| | | | | | | | |
| | | | | | | | |
| | | | | | | | |
| | | | | | | | |

# MICROFILM RESEARCH LOG

---------------------
FAMILY LINE

| Date ordered / Loan source | FILM TITLE / Call No. | Loan period From: To: | SEARCHING FOR / Date searched | RESULTS | Ref. No. |
|---|---|---|---|---|---|

# MICROFILM RESEARCH LOG

FAMILY LINE

| Date ordered / Loan source | FILM TITLE / Call No. | Loan period From: To: | SEARCHING FOR / Date searched | RESULTS | Ref. No. |
|---|---|---|---|---|---|
| | | | | | |
| | | | | | |
| | | | | | |
| | | | | | |
| | | | | | |
| | | | | | |
| | | | | | |
| | | | | | |
| | | | | | |
| | | | | | |
| | | | | | |
| | | | | | |
| | | | | | |
| | | | | | |
| | | | | | |
| | | | | | |
| | | | | | |
| | | | | | |

# MICROFILM RESEARCH LOG

______________ FAMILY LINE

| Date ordered / Loan source | FILM TITLE / Call No. | Loan period From: To: | SEARCHING FOR / Date searched | RESULTS | Ref. No. |
|---|---|---|---|---|---|
| | | | | | |
| | | | | | |
| | | | | | |
| | | | | | |
| | | | | | |
| | | | | | |
| | | | | | |
| | | | | | |
| | | | | | |
| | | | | | |
| | | | | | |
| | | | | | |
| | | | | | |
| | | | | | |
| | | | | | |
| | | | | | |
| | | | | | |
| | | | | | |

# MICROFILM RESEARCH LOG

FAMILY LINE ____________

| Date ordered / Loan source | FILM TITLE | Call No. | Loan period From: To: | SEARCHING FOR | Date searched | RESULTS | Ref. No. |
|---|---|---|---|---|---|---|---|
| | | | | | | | |
| | | | | | | | |
| | | | | | | | |
| | | | | | | | |
| | | | | | | | |
| | | | | | | | |
| | | | | | | | |
| | | | | | | | |
| | | | | | | | |
| | | | | | | | |
| | | | | | | | |
| | | | | | | | |
| | | | | | | | |
| | | | | | | | |
| | | | | | | | |
| | | | | | | | |
| | | | | | | | |
| | | | | | | | |

# MICROFILM RESEARCH LOG

__________________
FAMILY LINE

| Date ordered / Loan source | FILM TITLE | Call No. | Loan period From: To: | SEARCHING FOR | Date searched | RESULTS | Ref. No. |
|---|---|---|---|---|---|---|---|
| | | | | | | | |
| | | | | | | | |
| | | | | | | | |
| | | | | | | | |
| | | | | | | | |
| | | | | | | | |
| | | | | | | | |
| | | | | | | | |
| | | | | | | | |
| | | | | | | | |
| | | | | | | | |
| | | | | | | | |
| | | | | | | | |
| | | | | | | | |
| | | | | | | | |
| | | | | | | | |
| | | | | | | | |
| | | | | | | | |

# MICROFILM RESEARCH LOG

_______________ FAMILY LINE

| Date ordered / Loan source | FILM TITLE / Call No. | Loan period From: To: | SEARCHING FOR / Date searched | RESULTS | Ref. No. |
|---|---|---|---|---|---|
| | | | | | |
| | | | | | |
| | | | | | |
| | | | | | |
| | | | | | |
| | | | | | |
| | | | | | |
| | | | | | |
| | | | | | |
| | | | | | |
| | | | | | |
| | | | | | |
| | | | | | |
| | | | | | |
| | | | | | |
| | | | | | |
| | | | | | |
| | | | | | |

# MICROFILM RESEARCH LOG

______________________
FAMILY LINE

| Date ordered / Loan source | FILM TITLE | Call No. | Loan period From: To: | SEARCHING FOR | Date searched | RESULTS | Ref. No. |
|---|---|---|---|---|---|---|---|
| | | | | | | | |
| | | | | | | | |
| | | | | | | | |
| | | | | | | | |
| | | | | | | | |
| | | | | | | | |
| | | | | | | | |
| | | | | | | | |
| | | | | | | | |
| | | | | | | | |
| | | | | | | | |
| | | | | | | | |
| | | | | | | | |
| | | | | | | | |
| | | | | | | | |
| | | | | | | | |
| | | | | | | | |
| | | | | | | | |

# MICROFILM RESEARCH LOG

-----------------
FAMILY LINE

| Date ordered / Loan source | FILM TITLE / Call No. | Loan period From: To: | SEARCHING FOR / Date searched | RESULTS | Ref. No. |
|---|---|---|---|---|---|
| | | | | | |
| | | | | | |
| | | | | | |
| | | | | | |
| | | | | | |
| | | | | | |
| | | | | | |
| | | | | | |
| | | | | | |
| | | | | | |
| | | | | | |
| | | | | | |
| | | | | | |
| | | | | | |
| | | | | | |
| | | | | | |
| | | | | | |
| | | | | | |

# MICROFILM RESEARCH LOG

______________________
FAMILY LINE

| Date ordered / Loan source | FILM TITLE / Call No. | Loan period From: To: | SEARCHING FOR / Date searched | RESULTS | Ref. No. |
|---|---|---|---|---|---|
| | | | | | |
| | | | | | |
| | | | | | |
| | | | | | |
| | | | | | |
| | | | | | |
| | | | | | |
| | | | | | |
| | | | | | |
| | | | | | |
| | | | | | |
| | | | | | |
| | | | | | |
| | | | | | |
| | | | | | |
| | | | | | |
| | | | | | |
| | | | | | |

# MICROFILM RESEARCH LOG

____________________
FAMILY LINE

| Date ordered / Loan source | FILM TITLE | Call No. | Loan period From: To: | SEARCHING FOR | Date searched | RESULTS | Ref. No. |
|---|---|---|---|---|---|---|---|
| | | | | | | | |
| | | | | | | | |
| | | | | | | | |
| | | | | | | | |
| | | | | | | | |
| | | | | | | | |
| | | | | | | | |
| | | | | | | | |
| | | | | | | | |
| | | | | | | | |
| | | | | | | | |
| | | | | | | | |
| | | | | | | | |
| | | | | | | | |
| | | | | | | | |
| | | | | | | | |
| | | | | | | | |
| | | | | | | | |

# MICROFILM RESEARCH LOG ________________
FAMILY LINE

| Date ordered / Loan source | FILM TITLE | Call No. | Loan period From: To: | SEARCHING FOR | Date searched | RESULTS | Ref. No. |
|---|---|---|---|---|---|---|---|
| | | | | | | | |
| | | | | | | | |
| | | | | | | | |
| | | | | | | | |
| | | | | | | | |
| | | | | | | | |
| | | | | | | | |
| | | | | | | | |
| | | | | | | | |
| | | | | | | | |
| | | | | | | | |
| | | | | | | | |
| | | | | | | | |
| | | | | | | | |
| | | | | | | | |
| | | | | | | | |
| | | | | | | | |
| | | | | | | | |

# FAMILY GROUP RECORD

**HUSBAND** Occupation

| | |
|---|---|
| Born | Place |
| Chr. | Place |
| Marr. | Place |
| Died | Place |
| Bur. | Place |
| Father | Mother |
| Other Wives | |

**WIFE**

| | |
|---|---|
| Born | Place |
| Chr. | Place |
| Died | Place |
| Bur. | Place |
| Father | Mother |
| Other Husbands | |

| | Children | Sex | When Born / When Died | Where Born / Where Died | Marriage Date & Place / To Whom |
|---|---|---|---|---|---|
| 1 | | | | | |
| 2 | | | | | |
| 3 | | | | | |
| 4 | | | | | |
| 5 | | | | | |
| 6 | | | | | |
| 7 | | | | | |
| 8 | | | | | |
| 9 | | | | | |
| 10 | | | | | |
| 11 | | | | | |
| 12 | | | | | |
| 13 | | | | | |
| 14 | | | | | |
| 15 | | | | | |

Sources of Information

Other Marriages

**ORDER OF DATA**

NAME: John Henry BROWN
PLACE: Bramley, Hampshire, England
DATE: 2 September, 1832

# FAMILY GROUP RECORD

**HUSBAND** Occupation

| | | |
|---|---|---|
| Born | Place | |
| Chr. | Place | |
| Marr. | Place | |
| Died | Place | |
| Bur. | Place | |
| Father | | Mother |
| Other Wives | | |

**WIFE**

| | | |
|---|---|---|
| Born | Place | |
| Chr. | Place | |
| Died | Place | |
| Bur. | Place | |
| Father | | Mother |
| Other Husbands | | |

| | **Children** | Sex | When Born / When Died | Where Born / Where Died | Marriage Date & Place / To Whom |
|---|---|---|---|---|---|
| 1 | | | | | |
| 2 | | | | | |
| 3 | | | | | |
| 4 | | | | | |
| 5 | | | | | |
| 6 | | | | | |
| 7 | | | | | |
| 8 | | | | | |
| 9 | | | | | |
| 10 | | | | | |
| 11 | | | | | |
| 12 | | | | | |
| 13 | | | | | |
| 14 | | | | | |
| 15 | | | | | |

| Sources of Information | Other Marriages |
|---|---|

**ORDER OF DATA**

NAME: John Henry BROWN
PLACE: Bramley, Hampshire, England
DATE: 2 September, 1832

# FAMILY GROUP RECORD

**HUSBAND** | Occupation

| | | |
|---|---|---|
| Born | Place | |
| Chr. | Place | |
| Marr. | Place | |
| Died | Place | |
| Bur. | Place | |
| Father | | Mother |
| Other Wives | | |

**WIFE**

| | | |
|---|---|---|
| Born | Place | |
| Chr. | Place | |
| Died | Place | |
| Bur. | Place | |
| Father | | Mother |
| Other Husbands | | |

| | Children | Sex | When Born / When Died | Where Born / Where Died | Marriage Date & Place / To Whom |
|---|---|---|---|---|---|
| 1 | | | | | |
| 2 | | | | | |
| 3 | | | | | |
| 4 | | | | | |
| 5 | | | | | |
| 6 | | | | | |
| 7 | | | | | |
| 8 | | | | | |
| 9 | | | | | |
| 10 | | | | | |
| 11 | | | | | |
| 12 | | | | | |
| 13 | | | | | |
| 14 | | | | | |
| 15 | | | | | |

Sources of Information

Other Marriages

**ORDER OF DATA**

NAME: John Henry BROWN
PLACE: Bramley, Hampshire, England
DATE: 2 September, 1832

# FAMILY GROUP RECORD

**HUSBAND** Occupation

Born Place
Chr. Place
Marr. Place
Died Place
Bur. Place
Father Mother
Other Wives

**WIFE**

Born Place
Chr. Place
Died Place
Bur. Place
Father Mother
Other Husbands

| | **Children** | Sex | When Born / When Died | Where Born / Where Died | Marriage Date & Place / To Whom |
|---|---|---|---|---|---|
| 1 | | | | | |
| 2 | | | | | |
| 3 | | | | | |
| 4 | | | | | |
| 5 | | | | | |
| 6 | | | | | |
| 7 | | | | | |
| 8 | | | | | |
| 9 | | | | | |
| 10 | | | | | |
| 11 | | | | | |
| 12 | | | | | |
| 13 | | | | | |
| 14 | | | | | |
| 15 | | | | | |

Sources of Information

Other Marriages

**ORDER OF DATA**

NAME: John Henry BROWN
PLACE: Bramley, Hampshire, England
DATE: 2 September, 1832

# FAMILY GROUP RECORD

**HUSBAND** | Occupation

| | | | |
|---|---|---|---|
| Born | | Place | |
| Chr. | | Place | |
| Marr. | | Place | |
| Died | | Place | |
| Bur. | | Place | |
| Father | | Mother | |
| Other Wives | | | |

**WIFE**

| | | | |
|---|---|---|---|
| Born | | Place | |
| Chr. | | Place | |
| Died | | Place | |
| Bur. | | Place | |
| Father | | Mother | |
| Other Husbands | | | |

| | Children | Sex | When Born / When Died | Where Born / Where Died | Marriage Date & Place / To Whom |
|---|---|---|---|---|---|
| 1 | | | | | |
| 2 | | | | | |
| 3 | | | | | |
| 4 | | | | | |
| 5 | | | | | |
| 6 | | | | | |
| 7 | | | | | |
| 8 | | | | | |
| 9 | | | | | |
| 10 | | | | | |
| 11 | | | | | |
| 12 | | | | | |
| 13 | | | | | |
| 14 | | | | | |
| 15 | | | | | |

| Sources of Information | Other Marriages |
|---|---|
| | |

**ORDER OF DATA**

NAME: John Henry BROWN
PLACE: Bramley, Hampshire, England
DATE: 2 September, 1832

# FAMILY GROUP RECORD

**HUSBAND** Occupation

| | |
|---|---|
| Born | Place |
| Chr. | Place |
| Marr. | Place |
| Died | Place |
| Bur. | Place |
| Father | Mother |
| Other Wives | |

**WIFE**

| | |
|---|---|
| Born | Place |
| Chr. | Place |
| Died | Place |
| Bur. | Place |
| Father | Mother |
| Other Husbands | |

| | Children | Sex | When Born / When Died | Where Born / Where Died | Marriage Date & Place / To Whom |
|---|---|---|---|---|---|
| 1 | | | | | |
| 2 | | | | | |
| 3 | | | | | |
| 4 | | | | | |
| 5 | | | | | |
| 6 | | | | | |
| 7 | | | | | |
| 8 | | | | | |
| 9 | | | | | |
| 10 | | | | | |
| 11 | | | | | |
| 12 | | | | | |
| 13 | | | | | |
| 14 | | | | | |
| 15 | | | | | |

Sources of Information

Other Marriages

**ORDER OF DATA**

NAME: John Henry BROWN
PLACE: Bramley, Hampshire, England
DATE: 2 September, 1832

# FAMILY GROUP RECORD

**HUSBAND** Occupation

| | | |
|---|---|---|
| Born | Place | |
| Chr. | Place | |
| Marr. | Place | |
| Died | Place | |
| Bur. | Place | |
| Father | | Mother |
| Other Wives | | |

**WIFE**

| | | |
|---|---|---|
| Born | Place | |
| Chr. | Place | |
| Died | Place | |
| Bur. | Place | |
| Father | | Mother |
| Other Husbands | | |

| | Children | Sex | When Born / When Died | Where Born / Where Died | Marriage Date & Place / To Whom |
|---|---|---|---|---|---|
| 1 | | | | | |
| 2 | | | | | |
| 3 | | | | | |
| 4 | | | | | |
| 5 | | | | | |
| 6 | | | | | |
| 7 | | | | | |
| 8 | | | | | |
| 9 | | | | | |
| 10 | | | | | |
| 11 | | | | | |
| 12 | | | | | |
| 13 | | | | | |
| 14 | | | | | |
| 15 | | | | | |

| Sources of Information | Other Marriages |
|---|---|

**ORDER OF DATA**

NAME: John Henry BROWN
PLACE: Bramley, Hampshire, England
DATE: 2 September, 1832

# FAMILY GROUP RECORD

**HUSBAND** Occupation

Born Place

Chr. Place

Marr. Place

Died Place

Bur. Place

Father Mother

Other Wives

**WIFE**

Born Place

Chr. Place

Died Place

Bur. Place

Father Mother

Other Husbands

| | Children | Sex | When Born / When Died | Where Born / Where Died | Marriage Date & Place / To Whom |
|---|---|---|---|---|---|
| 1 | | | | | |
| 2 | | | | | |
| 3 | | | | | |
| 4 | | | | | |
| 5 | | | | | |
| 6 | | | | | |
| 7 | | | | | |
| 8 | | | | | |
| 9 | | | | | |
| 10 | | | | | |
| 11 | | | | | |
| 12 | | | | | |
| 13 | | | | | |
| 14 | | | | | |
| 15 | | | | | |

Sources of Information

Other Marriages

**ORDER OF DATA**

NAME: John Henry BROWN

PLACE: Bramley, Hampshire, England

DATE: 2 September, 1832

# FAMILY GROUP RECORD

**HUSBAND** Occupation

| | |
|---|---|
| Born | Place |
| Chr. | Place |
| Marr. | Place |
| Died | Place |
| Bur. | Place |
| Father | Mother |
| Other Wives | |

**WIFE**

| | |
|---|---|
| Born | Place |
| Chr. | Place |
| Died | Place |
| Bur. | Place |
| Father | Mother |
| Other Husbands | |

| | **Children** | Sex | When Born / When Died | Where Born / Where Died | Marriage Date & Place / To Whom |
|---|---|---|---|---|---|
| 1 | | | | | |
| 2 | | | | | |
| 3 | | | | | |
| 4 | | | | | |
| 5 | | | | | |
| 6 | | | | | |
| 7 | | | | | |
| 8 | | | | | |
| 9 | | | | | |
| 10 | | | | | |
| 11 | | | | | |
| 12 | | | | | |
| 13 | | | | | |
| 14 | | | | | |
| 15 | | | | | |

| Sources of Information | Other Marriages |
|---|---|
| | |

**ORDER OF DATA**

NAME: John Henry BROWN
PLACE: Bramley, Hampshire, England
DATE: 2 September, 1832

# FAMILY GROUP RECORD

**HUSBAND** Occupation

Born Place

Chr. Place

Marr. Place

Died Place

Bur. Place

Father Mother

Other Wives

**WIFE**

Born Place

Chr. Place

Died Place

Bur. Place

Father Mother

Other Husbands

| | **Children** | Sex | When Born / When Died | Where Born / Where Died | Marriage Date & Place / To Whom |
|---|---|---|---|---|---|
| 1 | | | | | |
| 2 | | | | | |
| 3 | | | | | |
| 4 | | | | | |
| 5 | | | | | |
| 6 | | | | | |
| 7 | | | | | |
| 8 | | | | | |
| 9 | | | | | |
| 10 | | | | | |
| 11 | | | | | |
| 12 | | | | | |
| 13 | | | | | |
| 14 | | | | | |
| 15 | | | | | |

Sources of Information

Other Marriages

**ORDER OF DATA**

NAME: John Henry BROWN

PLACE: Bramley, Hampshire, England

DATE: 2 September, 1832

# FAMILY GROUP RECORD

**HUSBAND** Occupation

| | |
|---|---|
| Born | Place |
| Chr. | Place |
| Marr. | Place |
| Died | Place |
| Bur. | Place |
| Father | Mother |
| Other Wives | |

**WIFE**

| | |
|---|---|
| Born | Place |
| Chr. | Place |
| Died | Place |
| Bur. | Place |
| Father | Mother |
| Other Husbands | |

| | Children | Sex | When Born / When Died | Where Born / Where Died | Marriage Date & Place / To Whom |
|---|---|---|---|---|---|
| 1 | | | | | |
| 2 | | | | | |
| 3 | | | | | |
| 4 | | | | | |
| 5 | | | | | |
| 6 | | | | | |
| 7 | | | | | |
| 8 | | | | | |
| 9 | | | | | |
| 10 | | | | | |
| 11 | | | | | |
| 12 | | | | | |
| 13 | | | | | |
| 14 | | | | | |
| 15 | | | | | |

Sources of Information

Other Marriages

**ORDER OF DATA**

NAME: John Henry BROWN
PLACE: Bramley, Hampshire, England
DATE: 2 September, 1832

# FAMILY GROUP RECORD

**HUSBAND** Occupation

| | | |
|---|---|---|
| Born | Place | |
| Chr. | Place | |
| Marr. | Place | |
| Died | Place | |
| Bur. | Place | |
| Father | | Mother |
| Other Wives | | |

**WIFE**

| | | |
|---|---|---|
| Born | Place | |
| Chr. | Place | |
| Died | Place | |
| Bur. | Place | |
| Father | | Mother |
| Other Husbands | | |

| | Children | Sex | When Born / When Died | Where Born / Where Died | Marriage Date & Place / To Whom |
|---|---|---|---|---|---|
| 1 | | | | | |
| 2 | | | | | |
| 3 | | | | | |
| 4 | | | | | |
| 5 | | | | | |
| 6 | | | | | |
| 7 | | | | | |
| 8 | | | | | |
| 9 | | | | | |
| 10 | | | | | |
| 11 | | | | | |
| 12 | | | | | |
| 13 | | | | | |
| 14 | | | | | |
| 15 | | | | | |

| Sources of Information | Other Marriages |
|---|---|
| | |

**ORDER OF DATA**

NAME: John Henry BROWN
PLACE: Bramley, Hampshire, England
DATE: 2 September, 1832

# FAMILY GROUP RECORD

**HUSBAND** Occupation

| | | |
|---|---|---|
| Born | Place | |
| Chr. | Place | |
| Marr. | Place | |
| Died | Place | |
| Bur. | Place | |
| Father | | Mother |
| Other Wives | | |

**WIFE**

| | | |
|---|---|---|
| Born | Place | |
| Chr. | Place | |
| Died | Place | |
| Bur. | Place | |
| Father | | Mother |
| Other Husbands | | |

| | Children | Sex | When Born / When Died | Where Born / Where Died | Marriage Date & Place / To Whom |
|---|---|---|---|---|---|
| 1 | | | | | |
| 2 | | | | | |
| 3 | | | | | |
| 4 | | | | | |
| 5 | | | | | |
| 6 | | | | | |
| 7 | | | | | |
| 8 | | | | | |
| 9 | | | | | |
| 10 | | | | | |
| 11 | | | | | |
| 12 | | | | | |
| 13 | | | | | |
| 14 | | | | | |
| 15 | | | | | |

Sources of Information

Other Marriages

**ORDER OF DATA**

NAME: John Henry BROWN
PLACE: Bramley, Hampshire, England
DATE: 2 September, 1832

# FAMILY GROUP RECORD

**HUSBAND** Occupation

| | | | |
|---|---|---|---|
| Born | | Place | |
| Chr. | | Place | |
| Marr. | | Place | |
| Died | | Place | |
| Bur. | | Place | |
| Father | | Mother | |
| Other Wives | | | |

**WIFE**

| | | | |
|---|---|---|---|
| Born | | Place | |
| Chr. | | Place | |
| Died | | Place | |
| Bur. | | Place | |
| Father | | Mother | |
| Other Husbands | | | |

| | Children | Sex | When Born<br>When Died | Where Born<br>Where Died | Marriage Date & Place<br>To Whom |
|---|---|---|---|---|---|
| 1 | | | | | |
| 2 | | | | | |
| 3 | | | | | |
| 4 | | | | | |
| 5 | | | | | |
| 6 | | | | | |
| 7 | | | | | |
| 8 | | | | | |
| 9 | | | | | |
| 10 | | | | | |
| 11 | | | | | |
| 12 | | | | | |
| 13 | | | | | |
| 14 | | | | | |
| 15 | | | | | |

Sources of Information

Other Marriages

**ORDER OF DATA**

NAME: John Henry BROWN
PLACE: Bramley, Hampshire, England
DATE: 2 September, 1832

# FAMILY GROUP RECORD

**HUSBAND** Occupation

| | |
|---|---|
| Born | Place |
| Chr. | Place |
| Marr. | Place |
| Died | Place |
| Bur. | Place |
| Father | Mother |
| Other Wives | |

**WIFE**

| | |
|---|---|
| Born | Place |
| Chr. | Place |
| Died | Place |
| Bur. | Place |
| Father | Mother |
| Other Husbands | |

| Children | Sex | When Born / When Died | Where Born / Where Died | Marriage Date & Place / To Whom |
|---|---|---|---|---|
| 1 | | | | |
| 2 | | | | |
| 3 | | | | |
| 4 | | | | |
| 5 | | | | |
| 6 | | | | |
| 7 | | | | |
| 8 | | | | |
| 9 | | | | |
| 10 | | | | |
| 11 | | | | |
| 12 | | | | |
| 13 | | | | |
| 14 | | | | |
| 15 | | | | |

Sources of Information

Other Marriages

**ORDER OF DATA**

NAME: John Henry BROWN
PLACE: Bramley, Hampshire, England
DATE: 2 September, 1832

# FAMILY GROUP RECORD

**HUSBAND** Occupation

| | | |
|---|---|---|
| Born | Place | |
| Chr. | Place | |
| Marr. | Place | |
| Died | Place | |
| Bur. | Place | |
| Father | | Mother |
| Other Wives | | |

**WIFE**

| | | |
|---|---|---|
| Born | Place | |
| Chr. | Place | |
| Died | Place | |
| Bur. | Place | |
| Father | | Mother |
| Other Husbands | | |

| | Children | Sex | When Born / When Died | Where Born / Where Died | Marriage Date & Place / To Whom |
|---|---|---|---|---|---|
| 1 | | | | | |
| 2 | | | | | |
| 3 | | | | | |
| 4 | | | | | |
| 5 | | | | | |
| 6 | | | | | |
| 7 | | | | | |
| 8 | | | | | |
| 9 | | | | | |
| 10 | | | | | |
| 11 | | | | | |
| 12 | | | | | |
| 13 | | | | | |
| 14 | | | | | |
| 15 | | | | | |

Sources of Information

Other Marriages

**ORDER OF DATA**

NAME: John Henry BROWN
PLACE: Bramley, Hampshire, England
DATE: 2 September, 1832

# FAMILY GROUP RECORD

**HUSBAND** Occupation

| | | |
|---|---|---|
| Born | Place | |
| Chr. | Place | |
| Marr. | Place | |
| Died | Place | |
| Bur. | Place | |
| Father | | Mother |
| Other Wives | | |

**WIFE**

| | | |
|---|---|---|
| Born | Place | |
| Chr. | Place | |
| Died | Place | |
| Bur. | Place | |
| Father | | Mother |
| Other Husbands | | |

| | Children | Sex | When Born / When Died | Where Born / Where Died | Marriage Date & Place / To Whom |
|---|---|---|---|---|---|
| 1 | | | | | |
| 2 | | | | | |
| 3 | | | | | |
| 4 | | | | | |
| 5 | | | | | |
| 6 | | | | | |
| 7 | | | | | |
| 8 | | | | | |
| 9 | | | | | |
| 10 | | | | | |
| 11 | | | | | |
| 12 | | | | | |
| 13 | | | | | |
| 14 | | | | | |
| 15 | | | | | |

| Sources of Information | Other Marriages |
|---|---|

**ORDER OF DATA**

NAME: John Henry BROWN
PLACE: Bramley, Hampshire, England
DATE: 2 September, 1832

# FAMILY GROUP RECORD

| **HUSBAND** | | Occupation |
|---|---|---|
| Born | Place | |
| Chr. | Place | |
| Marr. | Place | |
| Died | Place | |
| Bur. | Place | |
| Father | | Mother |
| Other Wives | | |

| **WIFE** | | |
|---|---|---|
| Born | Place | |
| Chr. | Place | |
| Died | Place | |
| Bur. | Place | |
| Father | | Mother |
| Other Husbands | | |

| | **Children** | Sex | When Born<br>When Died | Where Born<br>Where Died | Marriage Date & Place<br>To Whom |
|---|---|---|---|---|---|
| 1 | | | | | |
| 2 | | | | | |
| 3 | | | | | |
| 4 | | | | | |
| 5 | | | | | |
| 6 | | | | | |
| 7 | | | | | |
| 8 | | | | | |
| 9 | | | | | |
| 10 | | | | | |
| 11 | | | | | |
| 12 | | | | | |
| 13 | | | | | |
| 14 | | | | | |
| 15 | | | | | |

| Sources of Information | Other Marriages |
|---|---|
| | |

**ORDER OF DATA**

NAME: John Henry BROWN
PLACE: Bramley, Hampshire, England
DATE: 2 September, 1832

# FAMILY GROUP RECORD

**HUSBAND** Occupation

| | | |
|---|---|---|
| Born | Place | |
| Chr. | Place | |
| Marr. | Place | |
| Died | Place | |
| Bur. | Place | |
| Father | | Mother |
| Other Wives | | |

**WIFE**

| | | |
|---|---|---|
| Born | Place | |
| Chr. | Place | |
| Died | Place | |
| Bur. | Place | |
| Father | | Mother |
| Other Husbands | | |

| | Children | Sex | When Born / When Died | Where Born / Where Died | Marriage Date & Place / To Whom |
|---|---|---|---|---|---|
| 1 | | | | | |
| 2 | | | | | |
| 3 | | | | | |
| 4 | | | | | |
| 5 | | | | | |
| 6 | | | | | |
| 7 | | | | | |
| 8 | | | | | |
| 9 | | | | | |
| 10 | | | | | |
| 11 | | | | | |
| 12 | | | | | |
| 13 | | | | | |
| 14 | | | | | |
| 15 | | | | | |

| Sources of Information | Other Marriages |
|---|---|
| | |

**ORDER OF DATA**

NAME: John Henry BROWN
PLACE: Bramley, Hampshire, England
DATE: 2 September, 1832

# FAMILY GROUP RECORD

| **HUSBAND** | | Occupation |
|---|---|---|
| Born | Place | |
| Chr. | Place | |
| Marr. | Place | |
| Died | Place | |
| Bur. | Place | |
| Father | | Mother |
| Other Wives | | |

| **WIFE** | | |
|---|---|---|
| Born | Place | |
| Chr. | Place | |
| Died | Place | |
| Bur. | Place | |
| Father | | Mother |
| Other Husbands | | |

| | **Children** | Sex | When Born<br>When Died | Where Born<br>Where Died | Marriage Date & Place<br>To Whom |
|---|---|---|---|---|---|
| 1 | | | | | |
| 2 | | | | | |
| 3 | | | | | |
| 4 | | | | | |
| 5 | | | | | |
| 6 | | | | | |
| 7 | | | | | |
| 8 | | | | | |
| 9 | | | | | |
| 10 | | | | | |
| 11 | | | | | |
| 12 | | | | | |
| 13 | | | | | |
| 14 | | | | | |
| 15 | | | | | |

| Sources of Information | Other Marriages |
|---|---|
| | |

**ORDER OF DATA**

NAME: John Henry BROWN
PLACE: Bramley, Hampshire, England
DATE: 2 September, 1832

# FAMILY GROUP RECORD

**HUSBAND** Occupation

| | | |
|---|---|---|
| Born | Place | |
| Chr. | Place | |
| Marr. | Place | |
| Died | Place | |
| Bur. | Place | |
| Father | | Mother |
| Other Wives | | |

**WIFE**

| | | |
|---|---|---|
| Born | Place | |
| Chr. | Place | |
| Died | Place | |
| Bur. | Place | |
| Father | | Mother |
| Other Husbands | | |

| | Children | Sex | When Born / When Died | Where Born / Where Died | Marriage Date & Place / To Whom |
|---|---|---|---|---|---|
| 1 | | | | | |
| 2 | | | | | |
| 3 | | | | | |
| 4 | | | | | |
| 5 | | | | | |
| 6 | | | | | |
| 7 | | | | | |
| 8 | | | | | |
| 9 | | | | | |
| 10 | | | | | |
| 11 | | | | | |
| 12 | | | | | |
| 13 | | | | | |
| 14 | | | | | |
| 15 | | | | | |

Sources of Information

Other Marriages

**ORDER OF DATA**

NAME: John Henry BROWN
PLACE: Bramley, Hampshire, England
DATE: 2 September, 1832

# FAMILY GROUP RECORD

**HUSBAND** Occupation

| | | |
|---|---|---|
| Born | Place | |
| Chr. | Place | |
| Marr. | Place | |
| Died | Place | |
| Bur. | Place | |
| Father | | Mother |
| Other Wives | | |

**WIFE**

| | | |
|---|---|---|
| Born | Place | |
| Chr. | Place | |
| Died | Place | |
| Bur. | Place | |
| Father | | Mother |
| Other Husbands | | |

| | Children | Sex | When Born / When Died | Where Born / Where Died | Marriage Date & Place / To Whom |
|---|---|---|---|---|---|
| 1 | | | | | |
| 2 | | | | | |
| 3 | | | | | |
| 4 | | | | | |
| 5 | | | | | |
| 6 | | | | | |
| 7 | | | | | |
| 8 | | | | | |
| 9 | | | | | |
| 10 | | | | | |
| 11 | | | | | |
| 12 | | | | | |
| 13 | | | | | |
| 14 | | | | | |
| 15 | | | | | |

| Sources of Information | Other Marriages |
|---|---|
| | |

**ORDER OF DATA**

NAME: John Henry BROWN
PLACE: Bramley, Hampshire, England
DATE: 2 September, 1832

# FAMILY GROUP RECORD

**HUSBAND** Occupation

Born Place

Chr. Place

Marr. Place

Died Place

Bur. Place

Father Mother

Other Wives

**WIFE**

Born Place

Chr. Place

Died Place

Bur. Place

Father Mother

Other Husbands

| | **Children** | Sex | When Born / When Died | Where Born / Where Died | Marriage Date & Place / To Whom |
|---|---|---|---|---|---|
| 1 | | | | | |
| 2 | | | | | |
| 3 | | | | | |
| 4 | | | | | |
| 5 | | | | | |
| 6 | | | | | |
| 7 | | | | | |
| 8 | | | | | |
| 9 | | | | | |
| 10 | | | | | |
| 11 | | | | | |
| 12 | | | | | |
| 13 | | | | | |
| 14 | | | | | |
| 15 | | | | | |

Sources of Information

Other Marriages

**ORDER OF DATA**

NAME: John Henry BROWN

PLACE: Bramley, Hampshire, England

DATE: 2 September, 1832

# FAMILY GROUP RECORD

**HUSBAND** Occupation

| | | |
|---|---|---|
| Born | Place | |
| Chr. | Place | |
| Marr. | Place | |
| Died | Place | |
| Bur. | Place | |
| Father | | Mother |
| Other Wives | | |

**WIFE**

| | | |
|---|---|---|
| Born | Place | |
| Chr. | Place | |
| Died | Place | |
| Bur. | Place | |
| Father | | Mother |
| Other Husbands | | |

| | Children | Sex | When Born / When Died | Where Born / Where Died | Marriage Date & Place / To Whom |
|---|---|---|---|---|---|
| 1 | | | | | |
| 2 | | | | | |
| 3 | | | | | |
| 4 | | | | | |
| 5 | | | | | |
| 6 | | | | | |
| 7 | | | | | |
| 8 | | | | | |
| 9 | | | | | |
| 10 | | | | | |
| 11 | | | | | |
| 12 | | | | | |
| 13 | | | | | |
| 14 | | | | | |
| 15 | | | | | |

| Sources of Information | Other Marriages |
|---|---|

**ORDER OF DATA**

NAME: John Henry BROWN
PLACE: Bramley, Hampshire, England
DATE: 2 September, 1832

# FAMILY GROUP RECORD

**HUSBAND** Occupation

| | | |
|---|---|---|
| Born | Place | |
| Chr. | Place | |
| Marr. | Place | |
| Died | Place | |
| Bur. | Place | |
| Father | | Mother |
| Other Wives | | |

**WIFE**

| | | |
|---|---|---|
| Born | Place | |
| Chr. | Place | |
| Died | Place | |
| Bur. | Place | |
| Father | | Mother |
| Other Husbands | | |

| | Children | Sex | When Born / When Died | Where Born / Where Died | Marriage Date & Place / To Whom |
|---|---|---|---|---|---|
| 1 | | | | | |
| 2 | | | | | |
| 3 | | | | | |
| 4 | | | | | |
| 5 | | | | | |
| 6 | | | | | |
| 7 | | | | | |
| 8 | | | | | |
| 9 | | | | | |
| 10 | | | | | |
| 11 | | | | | |
| 12 | | | | | |
| 13 | | | | | |
| 14 | | | | | |
| 15 | | | | | |

| Sources of Information | Other Marriages |
|---|---|
| | |

**ORDER OF DATA**

NAME: John Henry BROWN
PLACE: Bramley, Hampshire, England
DATE: 2 September, 1832

# FAMILY GROUP RECORD

**HUSBAND** Occupation

| | | |
|---|---|---|
| Born | Place | |
| Chr. | Place | |
| Marr. | Place | |
| Died | Place | |
| Bur. | Place | |
| Father | | Mother |
| Other Wives | | |

**WIFE**

| | | |
|---|---|---|
| Born | Place | |
| Chr. | Place | |
| Died | Place | |
| Bur. | Place | |
| Father | | Mother |
| Other Husbands | | |

| | **Children** | Sex | When Born / When Died | Where Born / Where Died | Marriage Date & Place / To Whom |
|---|---|---|---|---|---|
| 1 | | | | | |
| 2 | | | | | |
| 3 | | | | | |
| 4 | | | | | |
| 5 | | | | | |
| 6 | | | | | |
| 7 | | | | | |
| 8 | | | | | |
| 9 | | | | | |
| 10 | | | | | |
| 11 | | | | | |
| 12 | | | | | |
| 13 | | | | | |
| 14 | | | | | |
| 15 | | | | | |

Sources of Information

Other Marriages

**ORDER OF DATA**

NAME: John Henry BROWN
PLACE: Bramley, Hampshire, England
DATE: 2 September, 1832

# FAMILY GROUP RECORD

**HUSBAND** Occupation

| | | |
|---|---|---|
| Born | Place | |
| Chr. | Place | |
| Marr. | Place | |
| Died | Place | |
| Bur. | Place | |
| Father | | Mother |
| Other Wives | | |

**WIFE**

| | | |
|---|---|---|
| Born | Place | |
| Chr. | Place | |
| Died | Place | |
| Bur. | Place | |
| Father | | Mother |
| Other Husbands | | |

| | Children | Sex | When Born / When Died | Where Born / Where Died | Marriage Date & Place / To Whom |
|---|---|---|---|---|---|
| 1 | | | | | |
| 2 | | | | | |
| 3 | | | | | |
| 4 | | | | | |
| 5 | | | | | |
| 6 | | | | | |
| 7 | | | | | |
| 8 | | | | | |
| 9 | | | | | |
| 10 | | | | | |
| 11 | | | | | |
| 12 | | | | | |
| 13 | | | | | |
| 14 | | | | | |
| 15 | | | | | |

| Sources of Information | Other Marriages |
|---|---|
| | |

**ORDER OF DATA**

NAME: John Henry BROWN
PLACE: Bramley, Hampshire, England
DATE: 2 September, 1832

# FAMILY GROUP RECORD

| **HUSBAND** | | Occupation |
|---|---|---|
| Born | Place | |
| Chr. | Place | |
| Marr. | Place | |
| Died | Place | |
| Bur. | Place | |
| Father | | Mother |
| Other Wives | | |

| **WIFE** | | |
|---|---|---|
| Born | Place | |
| Chr. | Place | |
| Died | Place | |
| Bur. | Place | |
| Father | | Mother |
| Other Husbands | | |

| | **Children** | Sex | When Born<br>When Died | Where Born<br>Where Died | Marriage Date & Place<br>To Whom |
|---|---|---|---|---|---|
| 1 | | | | | |
| 2 | | | | | |
| 3 | | | | | |
| 4 | | | | | |
| 5 | | | | | |
| 6 | | | | | |
| 7 | | | | | |
| 8 | | | | | |
| 9 | | | | | |
| 10 | | | | | |
| 11 | | | | | |
| 12 | | | | | |
| 13 | | | | | |
| 14 | | | | | |
| 15 | | | | | |

| Sources of Information | Other Marriages |
|---|---|
| | |

**ORDER OF DATA**

NAME: John Henry BROWN

PLACE: Bramley, Hampshire, England

DATE: 2 September, 1832

# FAMILY GROUP RECORD

**HUSBAND** Occupation

| | | | |
|---|---|---|---|
| Born | | Place | |
| Chr. | | Place | |
| Marr. | | Place | |
| Died | | Place | |
| Bur. | | Place | |
| Father | | Mother | |
| Other Wives | | | |

**WIFE**

| | | | |
|---|---|---|---|
| Born | | Place | |
| Chr. | | Place | |
| Died | | Place | |
| Bur. | | Place | |
| Father | | Mother | |
| Other Husbands | | | |

| | Children | Sex | When Born / When Died | Where Born / Where Died | Marriage Date & Place / To Whom |
|---|---|---|---|---|---|
| 1 | | | | | |
| 2 | | | | | |
| 3 | | | | | |
| 4 | | | | | |
| 5 | | | | | |
| 6 | | | | | |
| 7 | | | | | |
| 8 | | | | | |
| 9 | | | | | |
| 10 | | | | | |
| 11 | | | | | |
| 12 | | | | | |
| 13 | | | | | |
| 14 | | | | | |
| 15 | | | | | |

Sources of Information

Other Marriages

**ORDER OF DATA**

NAME: John Henry BROWN
PLACE: Bramley, Hampshire, England
DATE: 2 September, 1832

# FAMILY GROUP RECORD

**HUSBAND** Occupation

| | |
|---|---|
| Born | Place |
| Chr. | Place |
| Marr. | Place |
| Died | Place |
| Bur. | Place |
| Father | Mother |
| Other Wives | |

**WIFE**

| | |
|---|---|
| Born | Place |
| Chr. | Place |
| Died | Place |
| Bur. | Place |
| Father | Mother |
| Other Husbands | |

| Children | Sex | When Born / When Died | Where Born / Where Died | Marriage Date & Place / To Whom |
|---|---|---|---|---|
| 1 | | | | |
| 2 | | | | |
| 3 | | | | |
| 4 | | | | |
| 5 | | | | |
| 6 | | | | |
| 7 | | | | |
| 8 | | | | |
| 9 | | | | |
| 10 | | | | |
| 11 | | | | |
| 12 | | | | |
| 13 | | | | |
| 14 | | | | |
| 15 | | | | |

Sources of Information

Other Marriages

**ORDER OF DATA**

NAME: John Henry BROWN
PLACE: Bramley, Hampshire, England
DATE: 2 September, 1832

# FAMILY GROUP RECORD

**HUSBAND** Occupation

| | | |
|---|---|---|
| Born | Place | |
| Chr. | Place | |
| Marr. | Place | |
| Died | Place | |
| Bur. | Place | |
| Father | | Mother |
| Other Wives | | |

**WIFE**

| | | |
|---|---|---|
| Born | Place | |
| Chr. | Place | |
| Died | Place | |
| Bur. | Place | |
| Father | | Mother |
| Other Husbands | | |

| | Children | Sex | When Born / When Died | Where Born / Where Died | Marriage Date & Place / To Whom |
|---|---|---|---|---|---|
| 1 | | | | | |
| 2 | | | | | |
| 3 | | | | | |
| 4 | | | | | |
| 5 | | | | | |
| 6 | | | | | |
| 7 | | | | | |
| 8 | | | | | |
| 9 | | | | | |
| 10 | | | | | |
| 11 | | | | | |
| 12 | | | | | |
| 13 | | | | | |
| 14 | | | | | |
| 15 | | | | | |

Sources of Information

Other Marriages

**ORDER OF DATA**

NAME: John Henry BROWN
PLACE: Bramley, Hampshire, England
DATE: 2 September, 1832

# FAMILY GROUP RECORD

**HUSBAND** Occupation

| | |
|---|---|
| Born | Place |
| Chr. | Place |
| Marr. | Place |
| Died | Place |
| Bur. | Place |
| Father | Mother |
| Other Wives | |

**WIFE**

| | |
|---|---|
| Born | Place |
| Chr. | Place |
| Died | Place |
| Bur. | Place |
| Father | Mother |
| Other Husbands | |

| | **Children** | Sex | When Born / When Died | Where Born / Where Died | Marriage Date & Place / To Whom |
|---|---|---|---|---|---|
| 1 | | | | | |
| 2 | | | | | |
| 3 | | | | | |
| 4 | | | | | |
| 5 | | | | | |
| 6 | | | | | |
| 7 | | | | | |
| 8 | | | | | |
| 9 | | | | | |
| 10 | | | | | |
| 11 | | | | | |
| 12 | | | | | |
| 13 | | | | | |
| 14 | | | | | |
| 15 | | | | | |

Sources of Information

Other Marriages

**ORDER OF DATA**

NAME: John Henry BROWN
PLACE: Bramley, Hampshire, England
DATE: 2 September, 1832

# FAMILY GROUP RECORD

**HUSBAND** Occupation

| | |
|---|---|
| Born | Place |
| Chr. | Place |
| Marr. | Place |
| Died | Place |
| Bur. | Place |
| Father | Mother |
| Other Wives | |

**WIFE**

| | |
|---|---|
| Born | Place |
| Chr. | Place |
| Died | Place |
| Bur. | Place |
| Father | Mother |
| Other Husbands | |

| | Children | Sex | When Born<br>When Died | Where Born<br>Where Died | Marriage Date & Place<br>To Whom |
|---|---|---|---|---|---|
| 1 | | | | | |
| 2 | | | | | |
| 3 | | | | | |
| 4 | | | | | |
| 5 | | | | | |
| 6 | | | | | |
| 7 | | | | | |
| 8 | | | | | |
| 9 | | | | | |
| 10 | | | | | |
| 11 | | | | | |
| 12 | | | | | |
| 13 | | | | | |
| 14 | | | | | |
| 15 | | | | | |

| Sources of Information | Other Marriages |
|---|---|

**ORDER OF DATA**

NAME: John Henry BROWN
PLACE: Bramley, Hampshire, England
DATE: 2 September, 1832

# FAMILY GROUP RECORD

**HUSBAND** Occupation

| | | |
|---|---|---|
| Born | Place | |
| Chr. | Place | |
| Marr. | Place | |
| Died | Place | |
| Bur. | Place | |
| Father | | Mother |
| Other Wives | | |

**WIFE**

| | | |
|---|---|---|
| Born | Place | |
| Chr. | Place | |
| Died | Place | |
| Bur. | Place | |
| Father | | Mother |
| Other Husbands | | |

| | Children | Sex | When Born / When Died | Where Born / Where Died | Marriage Date & Place / To Whom |
|---|---|---|---|---|---|
| 1 | | | | | |
| 2 | | | | | |
| 3 | | | | | |
| 4 | | | | | |
| 5 | | | | | |
| 6 | | | | | |
| 7 | | | | | |
| 8 | | | | | |
| 9 | | | | | |
| 10 | | | | | |
| 11 | | | | | |
| 12 | | | | | |
| 13 | | | | | |
| 14 | | | | | |
| 15 | | | | | |

| Sources of Information | Other Marriages |
|---|---|

**ORDER OF DATA**

NAME: John Henry BROWN

PLACE: Bramley, Hampshire, England

DATE: 2 September, 1832

# FAMILY GROUP RECORD

**HUSBAND** Occupation

| | |
|---|---|
| Born | Place |
| Chr. | Place |
| Marr. | Place |
| Died | Place |
| Bur. | Place |
| Father | Mother |
| Other Wives | |

**WIFE**

| | |
|---|---|
| Born | Place |
| Chr. | Place |
| Died | Place |
| Bur. | Place |
| Father | Mother |
| Other Husbands | |

| | Children | Sex | When Born / When Died | Where Born / Where Died | Marriage Date & Place / To Whom |
|---|---|---|---|---|---|
| 1 | | | | | |
| 2 | | | | | |
| 3 | | | | | |
| 4 | | | | | |
| 5 | | | | | |
| 6 | | | | | |
| 7 | | | | | |
| 8 | | | | | |
| 9 | | | | | |
| 10 | | | | | |
| 11 | | | | | |
| 12 | | | | | |
| 13 | | | | | |
| 14 | | | | | |
| 15 | | | | | |

| Sources of Information | Other Marriages |
|---|---|
| | |

**ORDER OF DATA**

NAME: John Henry BROWN
PLACE: Bramley, Hampshire, England
DATE: 2 September, 1832

# FAMILY GROUP RECORD

**HUSBAND** Occupation

| | | |
|---|---|---|
| Born | Place | |
| Chr. | Place | |
| Marr. | Place | |
| Died | Place | |
| Bur. | Place | |
| Father | | Mother |
| Other Wives | | |

**WIFE**

| | | |
|---|---|---|
| Born | Place | |
| Chr. | Place | |
| Died | Place | |
| Bur. | Place | |
| Father | | Mother |
| Other Husbands | | |

| Children | Sex | When Born / When Died | Where Born / Where Died | Marriage Date & Place / To Whom |
|---|---|---|---|---|
| 1 | | | | |
| 2 | | | | |
| 3 | | | | |
| 4 | | | | |
| 5 | | | | |
| 6 | | | | |
| 7 | | | | |
| 8 | | | | |
| 9 | | | | |
| 10 | | | | |
| 11 | | | | |
| 12 | | | | |
| 13 | | | | |
| 14 | | | | |
| 15 | | | | |

| Sources of Information | Other Marriages |
|---|---|
| | |

**ORDER OF DATA**

NAME: John Henry BROWN

PLACE: Bramley, Hampshire, England

DATE: 2 September, 1832

# FAMILY GROUP RECORD

**HUSBAND** Occupation

| | | |
|---|---|---|
| Born | Place | |
| Chr. | Place | |
| Marr. | Place | |
| Died | Place | |
| Bur. | Place | |
| Father | | Mother |
| Other Wives | | |

**WIFE**

| | | |
|---|---|---|
| Born | Place | |
| Chr. | Place | |
| Died | Place | |
| Bur. | Place | |
| Father | | Mother |
| Other Husbands | | |

| | Children | Sex | When Born / When Died | Where Born / Where Died | Marriage Date & Place / To Whom |
|---|---|---|---|---|---|
| 1 | | | | | |
| 2 | | | | | |
| 3 | | | | | |
| 4 | | | | | |
| 5 | | | | | |
| 6 | | | | | |
| 7 | | | | | |
| 8 | | | | | |
| 9 | | | | | |
| 10 | | | | | |
| 11 | | | | | |
| 12 | | | | | |
| 13 | | | | | |
| 14 | | | | | |
| 15 | | | | | |

| Sources of Information | Other Marriages |
|---|---|
| | |

**ORDER OF DATA**

NAME: John Henry BROWN
PLACE: Bramley, Hampshire, England
DATE: 2 September, 1832

# FAMILY GROUP RECORD

**HUSBAND** Occupation

| | | | |
|---|---|---|---|
| Born | | Place | |
| Chr. | | Place | |
| Marr. | | Place | |
| Died | | Place | |
| Bur. | | Place | |
| Father | | Mother | |
| Other Wives | | | |

**WIFE**

| | | | |
|---|---|---|---|
| Born | | Place | |
| Chr. | | Place | |
| Died | | Place | |
| Bur. | | Place | |
| Father | | Mother | |
| Other Husbands | | | |

| | **Children** | Sex | When Born / When Died | Where Born / Where Died | Marriage Date & Place / To Whom |
|---|---|---|---|---|---|
| 1 | | | | | |
| 2 | | | | | |
| 3 | | | | | |
| 4 | | | | | |
| 5 | | | | | |
| 6 | | | | | |
| 7 | | | | | |
| 8 | | | | | |
| 9 | | | | | |
| 10 | | | | | |
| 11 | | | | | |
| 12 | | | | | |
| 13 | | | | | |
| 14 | | | | | |
| 15 | | | | | |

| Sources of Information | Other Marriages |
|---|---|
| | |

**ORDER OF DATA**

NAME: John Henry BROWN

PLACE: Bramley, Hampshire, England

DATE: 2 September, 1832

# FAMILY GROUP RECORD

**HUSBAND** Occupation

Born Place

Chr. Place

Marr. Place

Died Place

Bur. Place

Father Mother

Other Wives

**WIFE**

Born Place

Chr. Place

Died Place

Bur. Place

Father Mother

Other Husbands

| | **Children** | Sex | When Born / When Died | Where Born / Where Died | Marriage Date & Place / To Whom |
|---|---|---|---|---|---|
| 1 | | | | | |
| 2 | | | | | |
| 3 | | | | | |
| 4 | | | | | |
| 5 | | | | | |
| 6 | | | | | |
| 7 | | | | | |
| 8 | | | | | |
| 9 | | | | | |
| 10 | | | | | |
| 11 | | | | | |
| 12 | | | | | |
| 13 | | | | | |
| 14 | | | | | |
| 15 | | | | | |

Sources of Information

Other Marriages

**ORDER OF DATA**

NAME: John Henry BROWN

PLACE: Bramley, Hampshire, England

DATE: 2 September, 1832

# FAMILY GROUP RECORD

**HUSBAND** Occupation

| | | |
|---|---|---|
| Born | Place | |
| Chr. | Place | |
| Marr. | Place | |
| Died | Place | |
| Bur. | Place | |
| Father | | Mother |
| Other Wives | | |

**WIFE**

| | | |
|---|---|---|
| Born | Place | |
| Chr. | Place | |
| Died | Place | |
| Bur. | Place | |
| Father | | Mother |
| Other Husbands | | |

| | Children | Sex | When Born / When Died | Where Born / Where Died | Marriage Date & Place / To Whom |
|---|---|---|---|---|---|
| 1 | | | | | |
| 2 | | | | | |
| 3 | | | | | |
| 4 | | | | | |
| 5 | | | | | |
| 6 | | | | | |
| 7 | | | | | |
| 8 | | | | | |
| 9 | | | | | |
| 10 | | | | | |
| 11 | | | | | |
| 12 | | | | | |
| 13 | | | | | |
| 14 | | | | | |
| 15 | | | | | |

| Sources of Information | Other Marriages |
|---|---|
| | |

**ORDER OF DATA**

NAME: John Henry BROWN
PLACE: Bramley, Hampshire, England
DATE: 2 September, 1832

# PEDIGREE CHART

CHART NO. ______

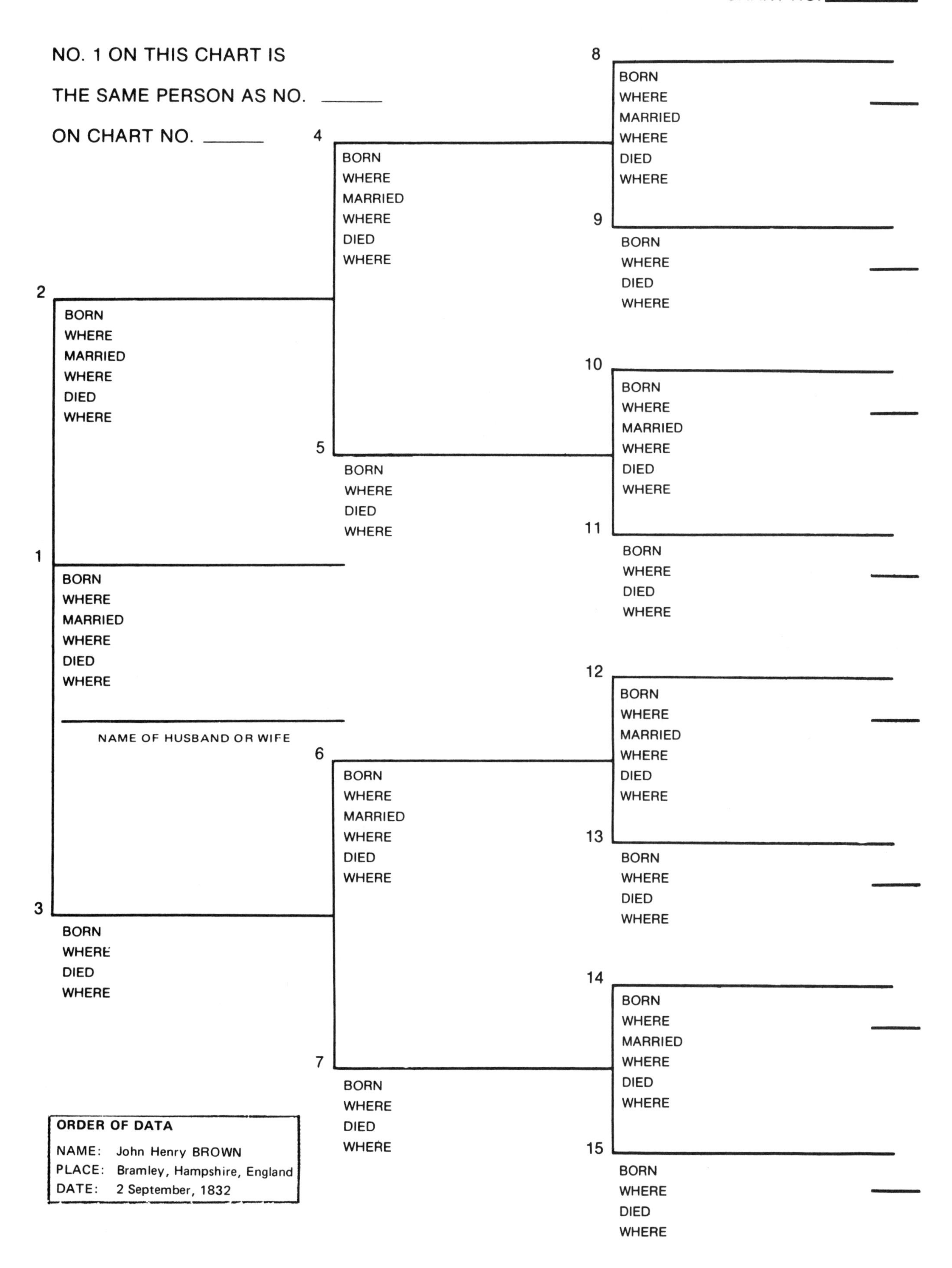

NO. 1 ON THIS CHART IS

THE SAME PERSON AS NO. ______

ON CHART NO. ______

1
BORN
WHERE
MARRIED
WHERE
DIED
WHERE

NAME OF HUSBAND OR WIFE

2
BORN
WHERE
MARRIED
WHERE
DIED
WHERE

3
BORN
WHERE
DIED
WHERE

4
BORN
WHERE
MARRIED
WHERE
DIED
WHERE

5
BORN
WHERE
DIED
WHERE

6
BORN
WHERE
MARRIED
WHERE
DIED
WHERE

7
BORN
WHERE
DIED
WHERE

8
BORN
WHERE
MARRIED
WHERE
DIED
WHERE

9
BORN
WHERE
DIED
WHERE

10
BORN
WHERE
MARRIED
WHERE
DIED
WHERE

11
BORN
WHERE
DIED
WHERE

12
BORN
WHERE
MARRIED
WHERE
DIED
WHERE

13
BORN
WHERE
DIED
WHERE

14
BORN
WHERE
MARRIED
WHERE
DIED
WHERE

15
BORN
WHERE
DIED
WHERE

**ORDER OF DATA**

NAME: John Henry BROWN
PLACE: Bramley, Hampshire, England
DATE: 2 September, 1832

# PEDIGREE CHART

CHART NO. ______

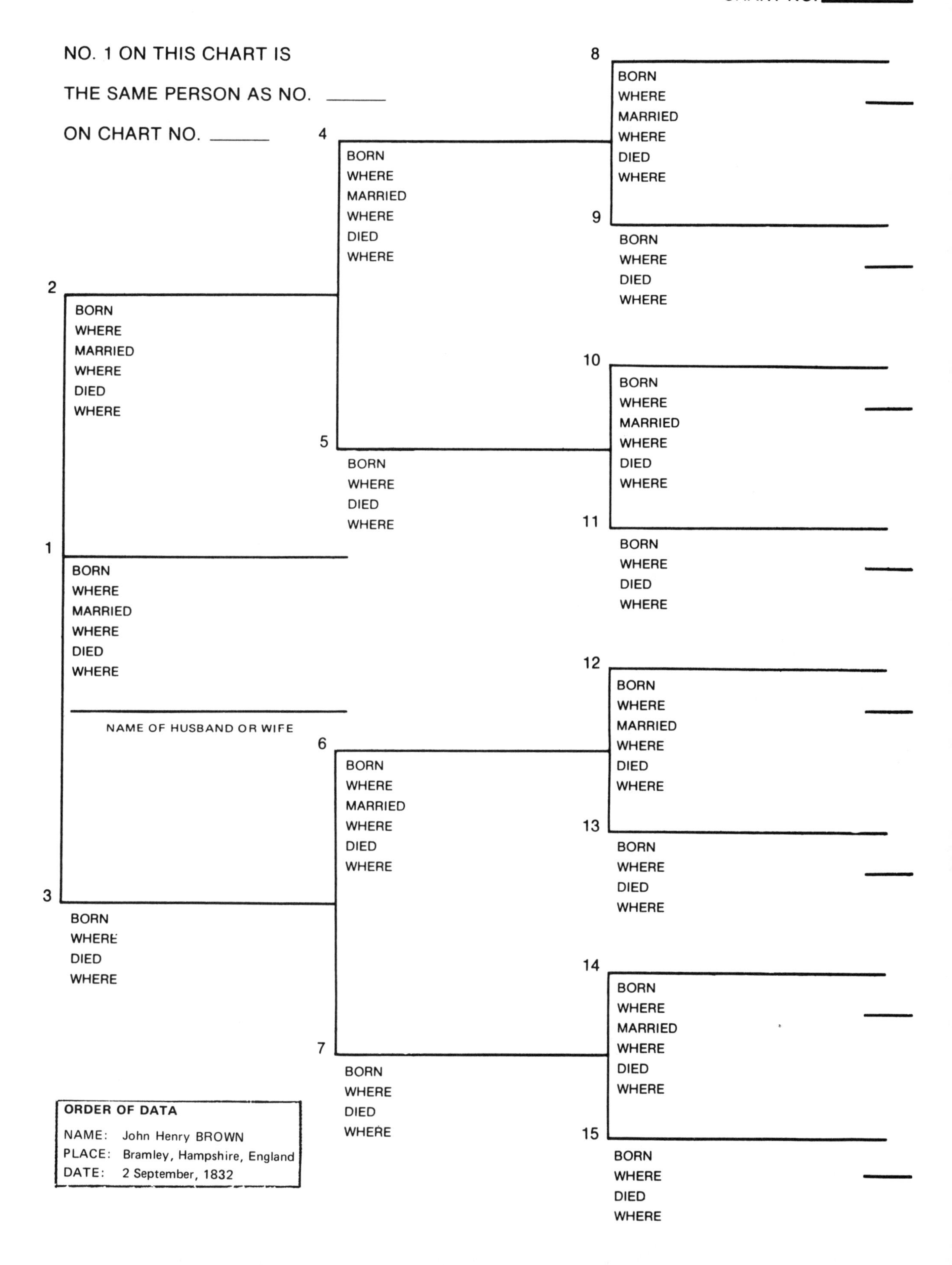

NO. 1 ON THIS CHART IS

THE SAME PERSON AS NO. ______

ON CHART NO. ______

8
BORN
WHERE
MARRIED
WHERE
DIED
WHERE

4
BORN
WHERE
MARRIED
WHERE
DIED
WHERE

9
BORN
WHERE
DIED
WHERE

2
BORN
WHERE
MARRIED
WHERE
DIED
WHERE

10
BORN
WHERE
MARRIED
WHERE
DIED
WHERE

5
BORN
WHERE
DIED
WHERE

11
BORN
WHERE
DIED
WHERE

1
BORN
WHERE
MARRIED
WHERE
DIED
WHERE

NAME OF HUSBAND OR WIFE

12
BORN
WHERE
MARRIED
WHERE
DIED
WHERE

6
BORN
WHERE
MARRIED
WHERE
DIED
WHERE

13
BORN
WHERE
DIED
WHERE

3
BORN
WHERE
DIED
WHERE

14
BORN
WHERE
MARRIED
WHERE
DIED
WHERE

7
BORN
WHERE
DIED
WHERE

15
BORN
WHERE
DIED
WHERE

**ORDER OF DATA**

NAME: John Henry BROWN
PLACE: Bramley, Hampshire, England
DATE: 2 September, 1832

# PEDIGREE CHART

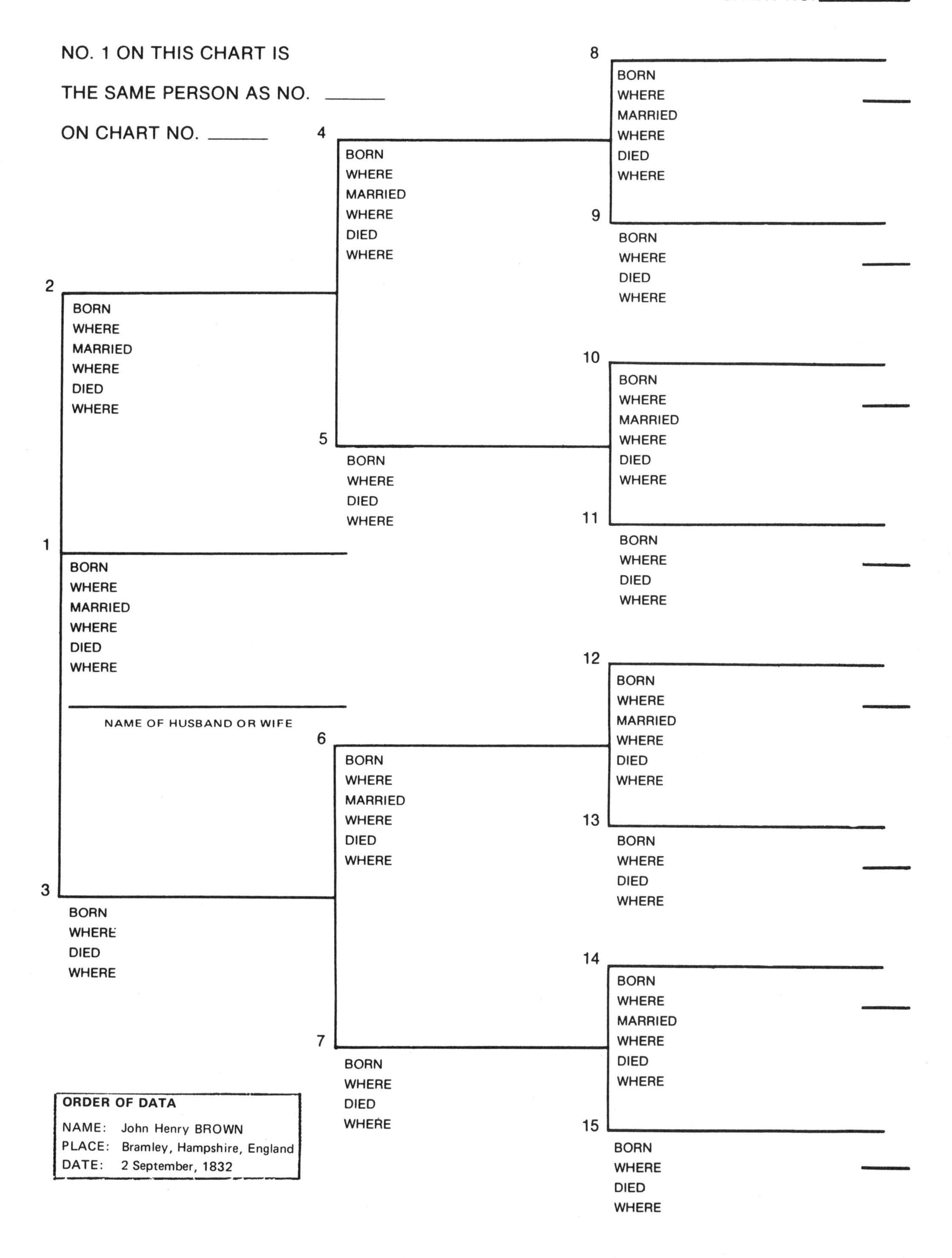

# PEDIGREE CHART

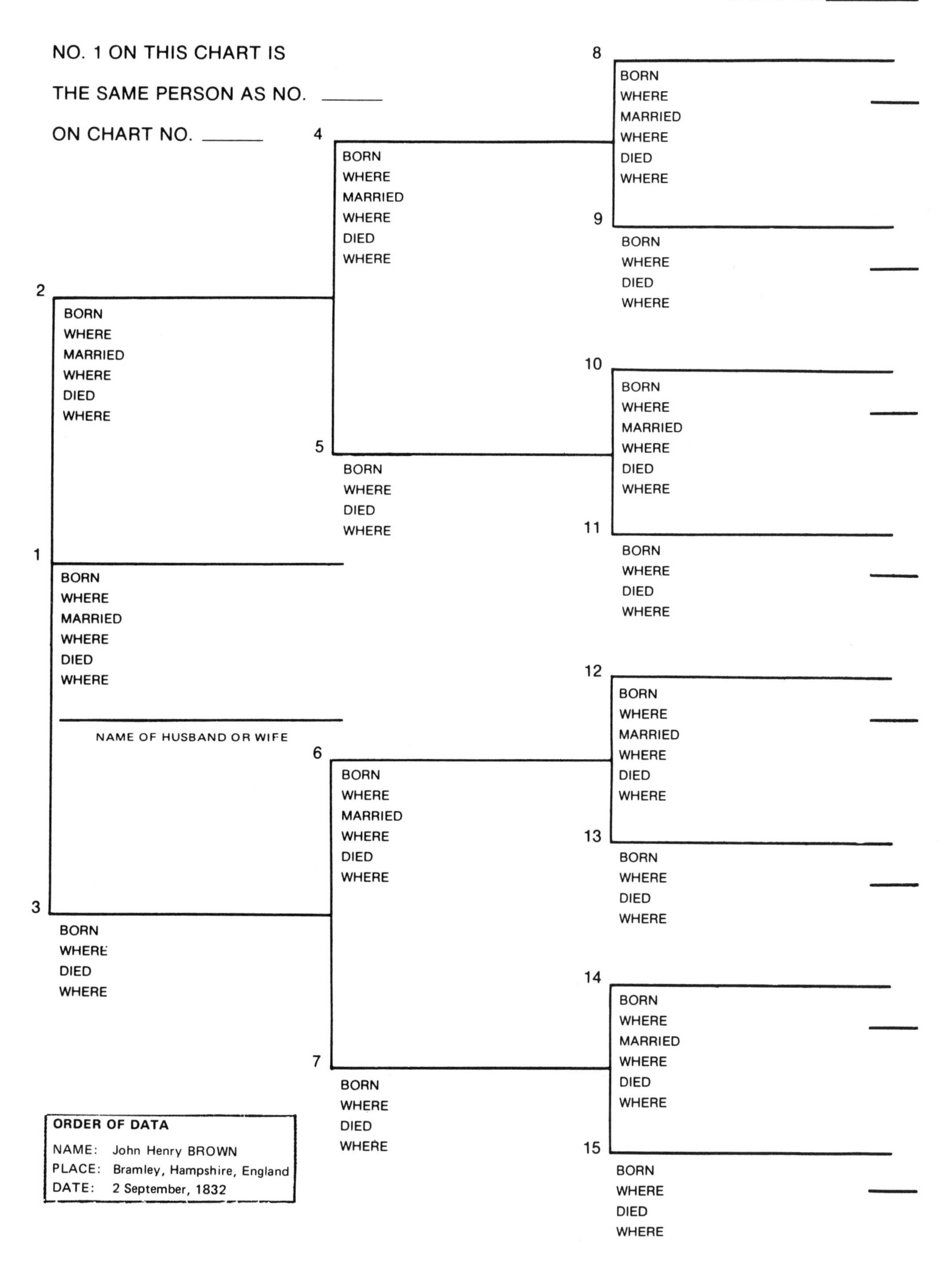

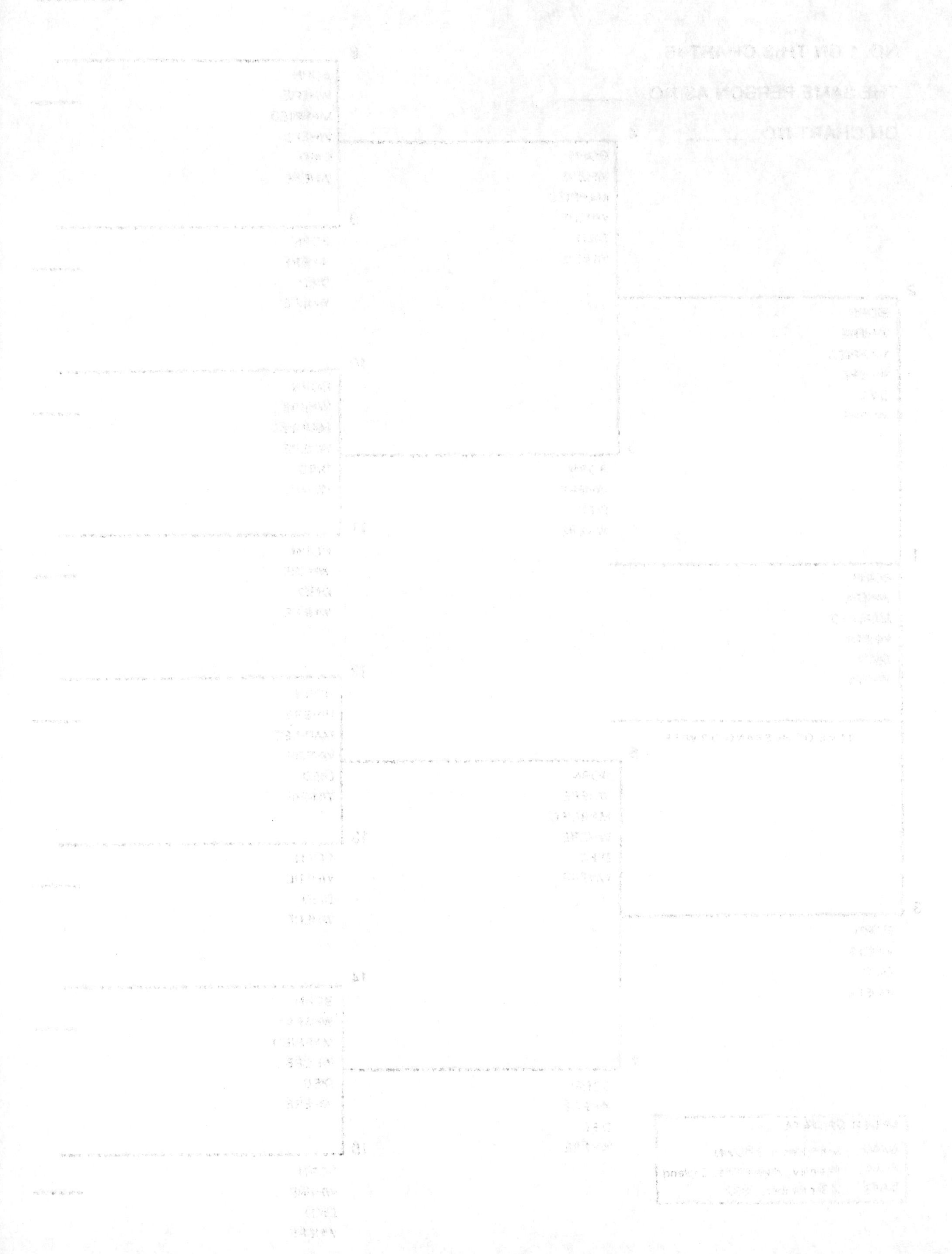

# PEDIGREE CHART

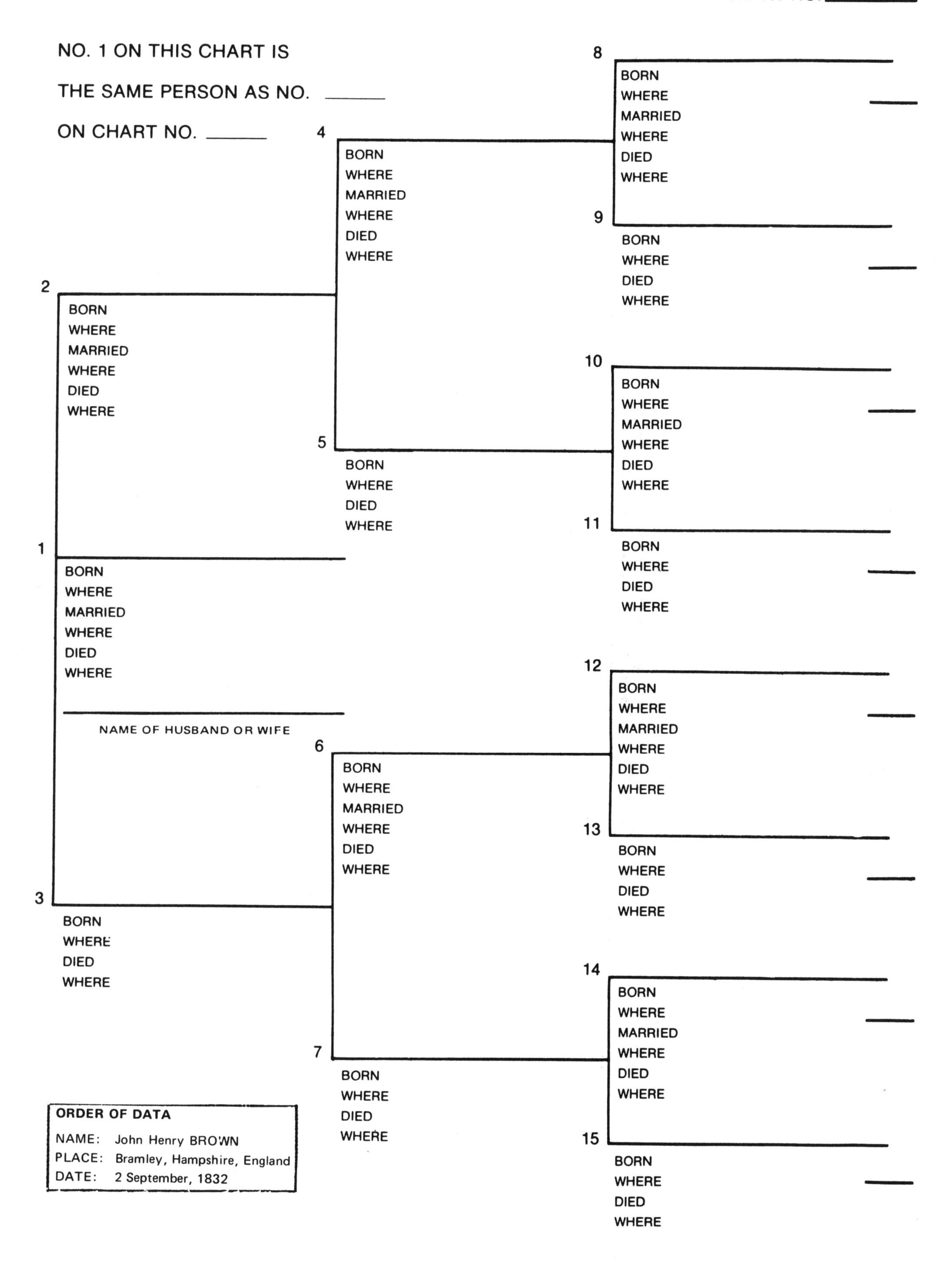

CHART NO. ______

NO. 1 ON THIS CHART IS

THE SAME PERSON AS NO. ______

ON CHART NO. ______

1
BORN
WHERE
MARRIED
WHERE
DIED
WHERE

NAME OF HUSBAND OR WIFE

2
BORN
WHERE
MARRIED
WHERE
DIED
WHERE

3
BORN
WHERE
DIED
WHERE

4
BORN
WHERE
MARRIED
WHERE
DIED
WHERE

5
BORN
WHERE
DIED
WHERE

6
BORN
WHERE
MARRIED
WHERE
DIED
WHERE

7
BORN
WHERE
DIED
WHERE

8
BORN
WHERE
MARRIED
WHERE
DIED
WHERE

9
BORN
WHERE
DIED
WHERE

10
BORN
WHERE
MARRIED
WHERE
DIED
WHERE

11
BORN
WHERE
DIED
WHERE

12
BORN
WHERE
MARRIED
WHERE
DIED
WHERE

13
BORN
WHERE
DIED
WHERE

14
BORN
WHERE
MARRIED
WHERE
DIED
WHERE

15
BORN
WHERE
DIED
WHERE

**ORDER OF DATA**

NAME: John Henry BROWN
PLACE: Bramley, Hampshire, England
DATE: 2 September, 1832

# PEDIGREE CHART

CHART NO. ______

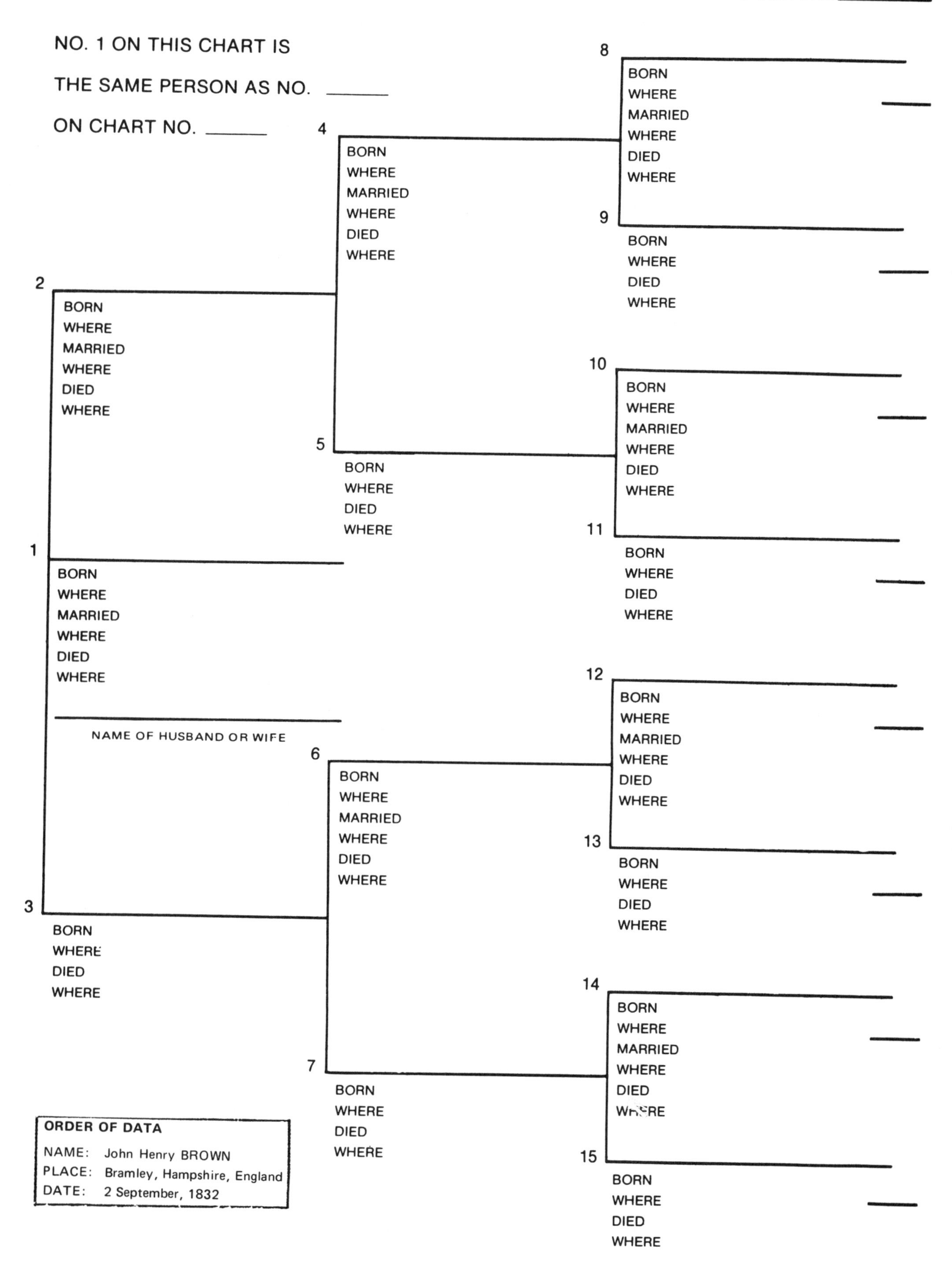

NO. 1 ON THIS CHART IS
THE SAME PERSON AS NO. ______
ON CHART NO. ______

1
BORN
WHERE
MARRIED
WHERE
DIED
WHERE

NAME OF HUSBAND OR WIFE

2
BORN
WHERE
MARRIED
WHERE
DIED
WHERE

3
BORN
WHERE
DIED
WHERE

4
BORN
WHERE
MARRIED
WHERE
DIED
WHERE

5
BORN
WHERE
DIED
WHERE

6
BORN
WHERE
MARRIED
WHERE
DIED
WHERE

7
BORN
WHERE
DIED
WHERE

8
BORN
WHERE
MARRIED
WHERE
DIED
WHERE

9
BORN
WHERE
DIED
WHERE

10
BORN
WHERE
MARRIED
WHERE
DIED
WHERE

11
BORN
WHERE
DIED
WHERE

12
BORN
WHERE
MARRIED
WHERE
DIED
WHERE

13
BORN
WHERE
DIED
WHERE

14
BORN
WHERE
MARRIED
WHERE
DIED
WHERE

15
BORN
WHERE
DIED
WHERE

ORDER OF DATA
NAME: John Henry BROWN
PLACE: Bramley, Hampshire, England
DATE: 2 September, 1832

# PEDIGREE CHART

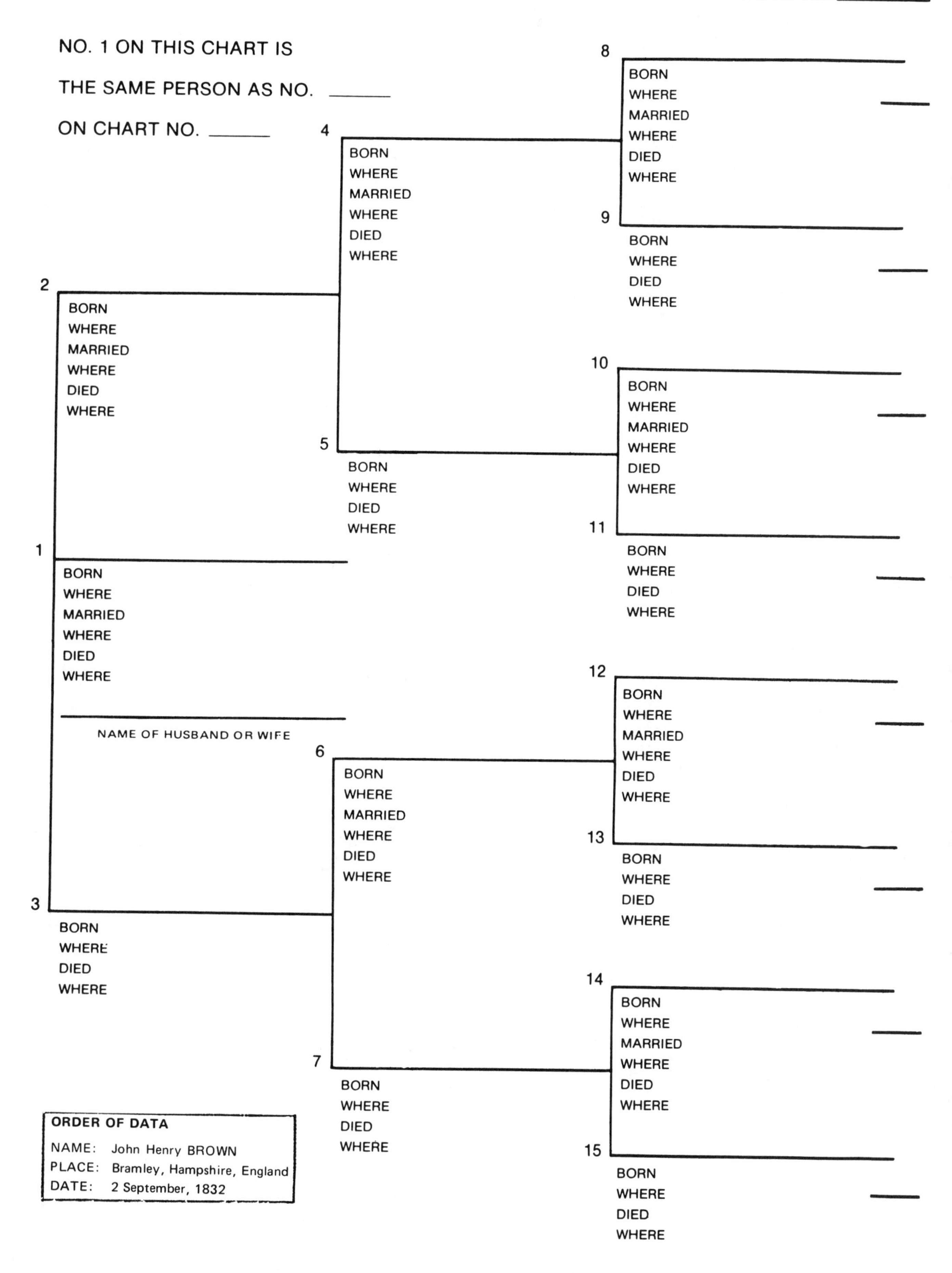

# PEDIGREE CHART

CHART NO. ______

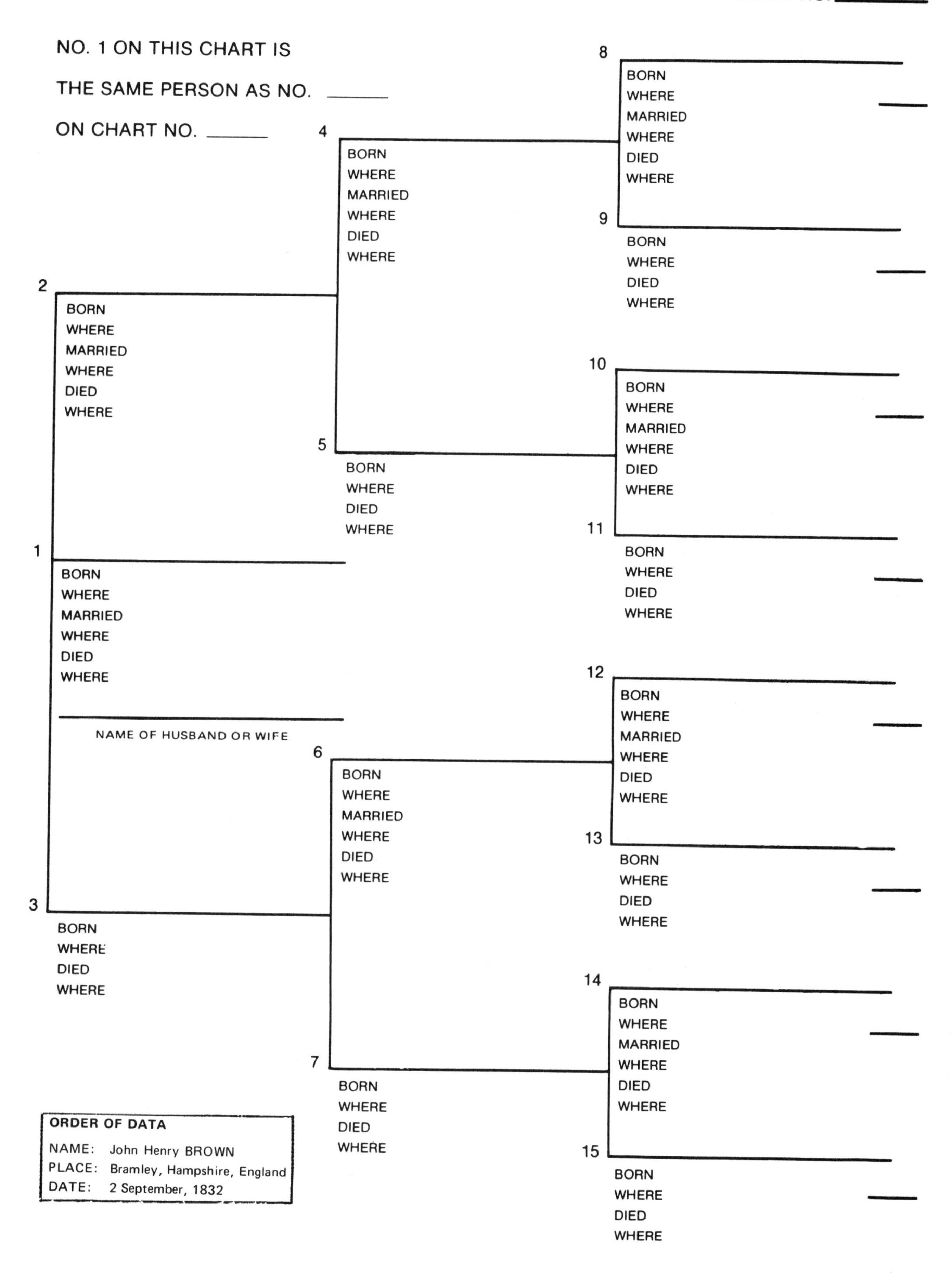

NO. 1 ON THIS CHART IS
THE SAME PERSON AS NO. ______
ON CHART NO. ______

1
BORN
WHERE
MARRIED
WHERE
DIED
WHERE

NAME OF HUSBAND OR WIFE

2
BORN
WHERE
MARRIED
WHERE
DIED
WHERE

3
BORN
WHERE
DIED
WHERE

4
BORN
WHERE
MARRIED
WHERE
DIED
WHERE

5
BORN
WHERE
DIED
WHERE

6
BORN
WHERE
MARRIED
WHERE
DIED
WHERE

7
BORN
WHERE
DIED
WHERE

8
BORN
WHERE
MARRIED
WHERE
DIED
WHERE

9
BORN
WHERE
DIED
WHERE

10
BORN
WHERE
MARRIED
WHERE
DIED
WHERE

11
BORN
WHERE
DIED
WHERE

12
BORN
WHERE
MARRIED
WHERE
DIED
WHERE

13
BORN
WHERE
DIED
WHERE

14
BORN
WHERE
MARRIED
WHERE
DIED
WHERE

15
BORN
WHERE
DIED
WHERE

**ORDER OF DATA**
NAME: John Henry BROWN
PLACE: Bramley, Hampshire, England
DATE: 2 September, 1832

# PEDIGREE CHART

CHART NO. ______

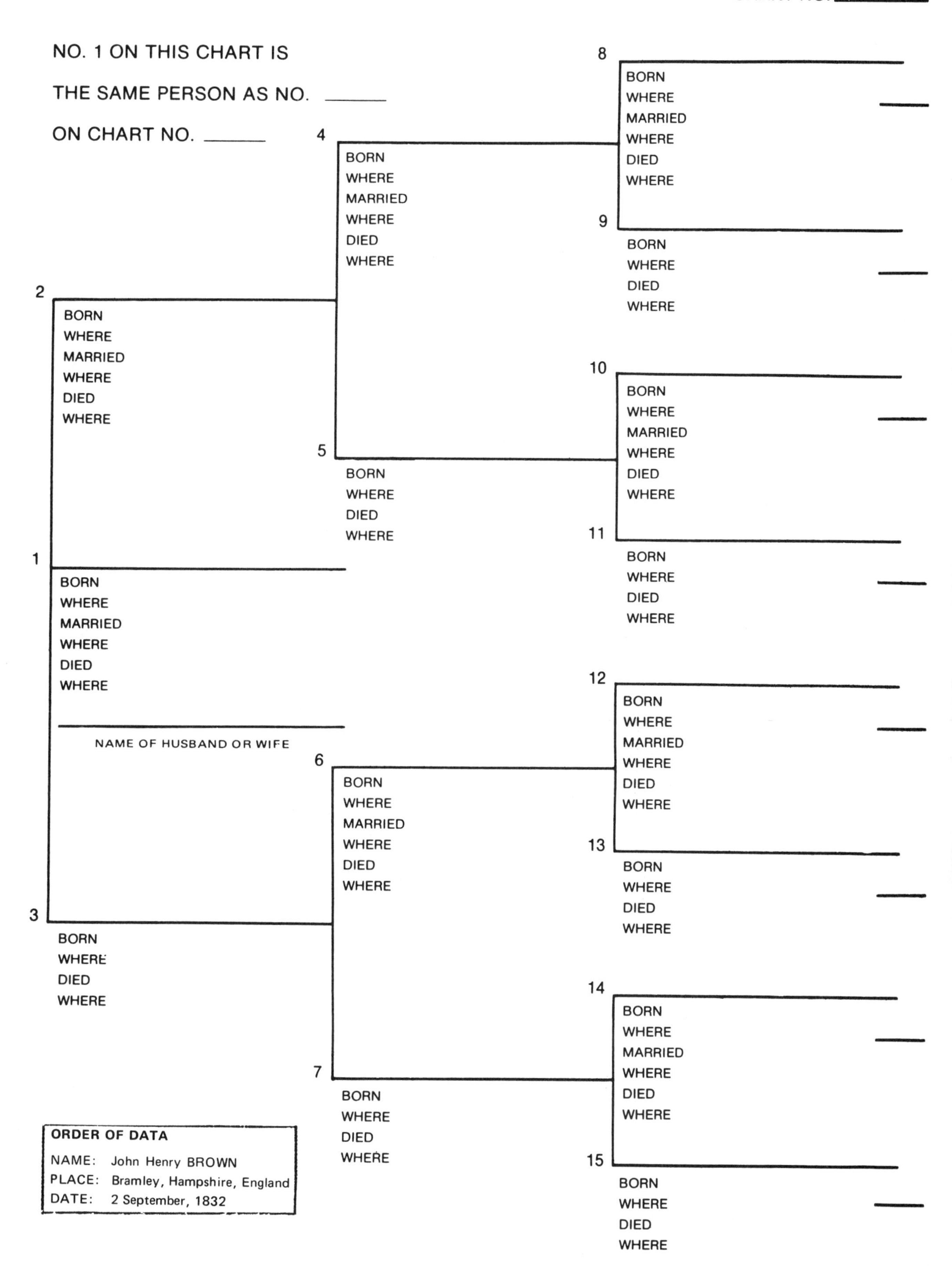

NO. 1 ON THIS CHART IS

THE SAME PERSON AS NO. ______

ON CHART NO. ______

2
BORN
WHERE
MARRIED
WHERE
DIED
WHERE

1
BORN
WHERE
MARRIED
WHERE
DIED
WHERE

NAME OF HUSBAND OR WIFE

3
BORN
WHERE
DIED
WHERE

4
BORN
WHERE
MARRIED
WHERE
DIED
WHERE

5
BORN
WHERE
DIED
WHERE

6
BORN
WHERE
MARRIED
WHERE
DIED
WHERE

7
BORN
WHERE
DIED
WHERE

8
BORN
WHERE
MARRIED
WHERE
DIED
WHERE

9
BORN
WHERE
DIED
WHERE

10
BORN
WHERE
MARRIED
WHERE
DIED
WHERE

11
BORN
WHERE
DIED
WHERE

12
BORN
WHERE
MARRIED
WHERE
DIED
WHERE

13
BORN
WHERE
DIED
WHERE

14
BORN
WHERE
MARRIED
WHERE
DIED
WHERE

15
BORN
WHERE
DIED
WHERE

**ORDER OF DATA**

NAME: John Henry BROWN
PLACE: Bramley, Hampshire, England
DATE: 2 September, 1832

# PEDIGREE CHART

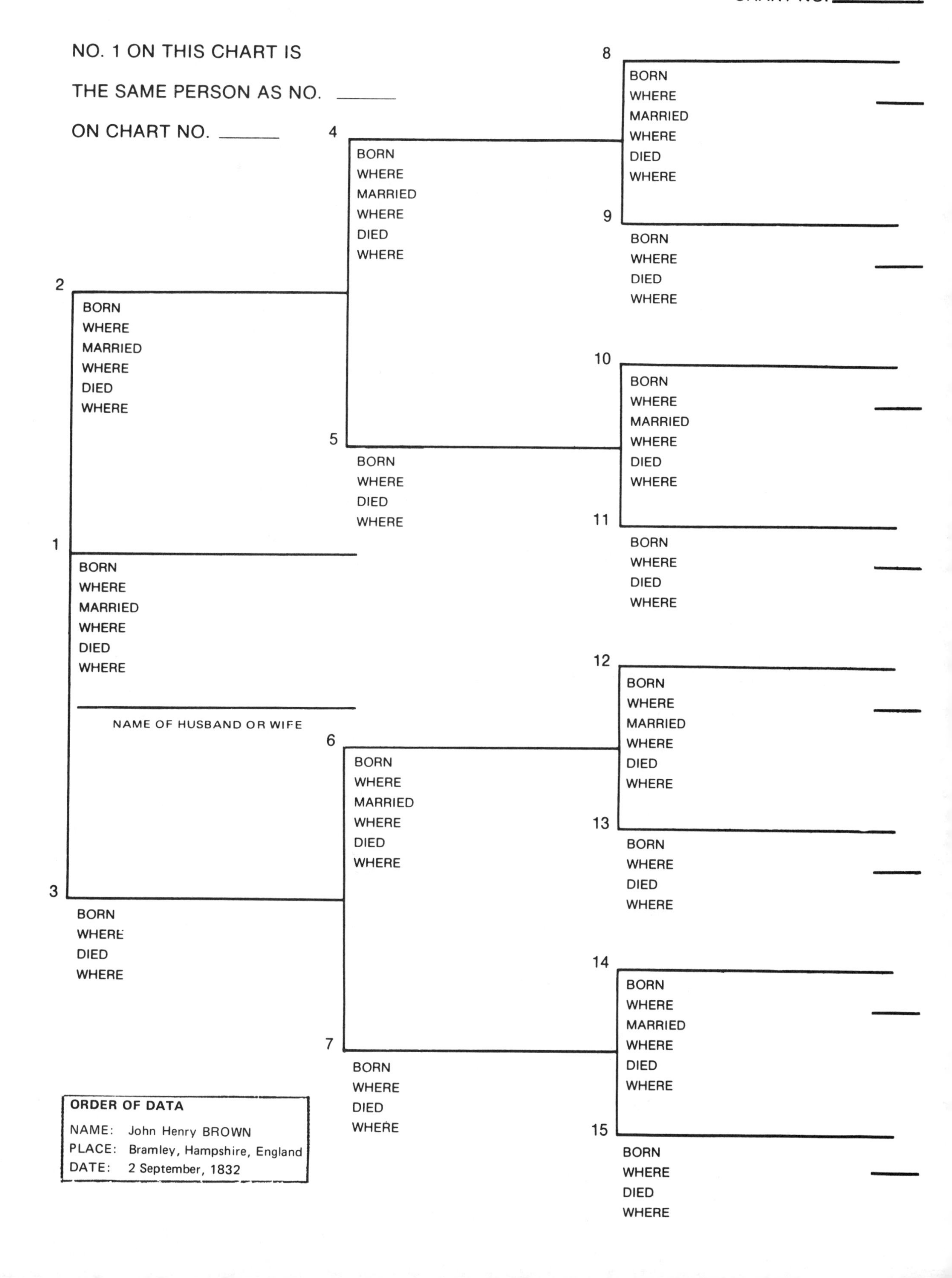

# PEDIGREE CHART

CHART NO. ______

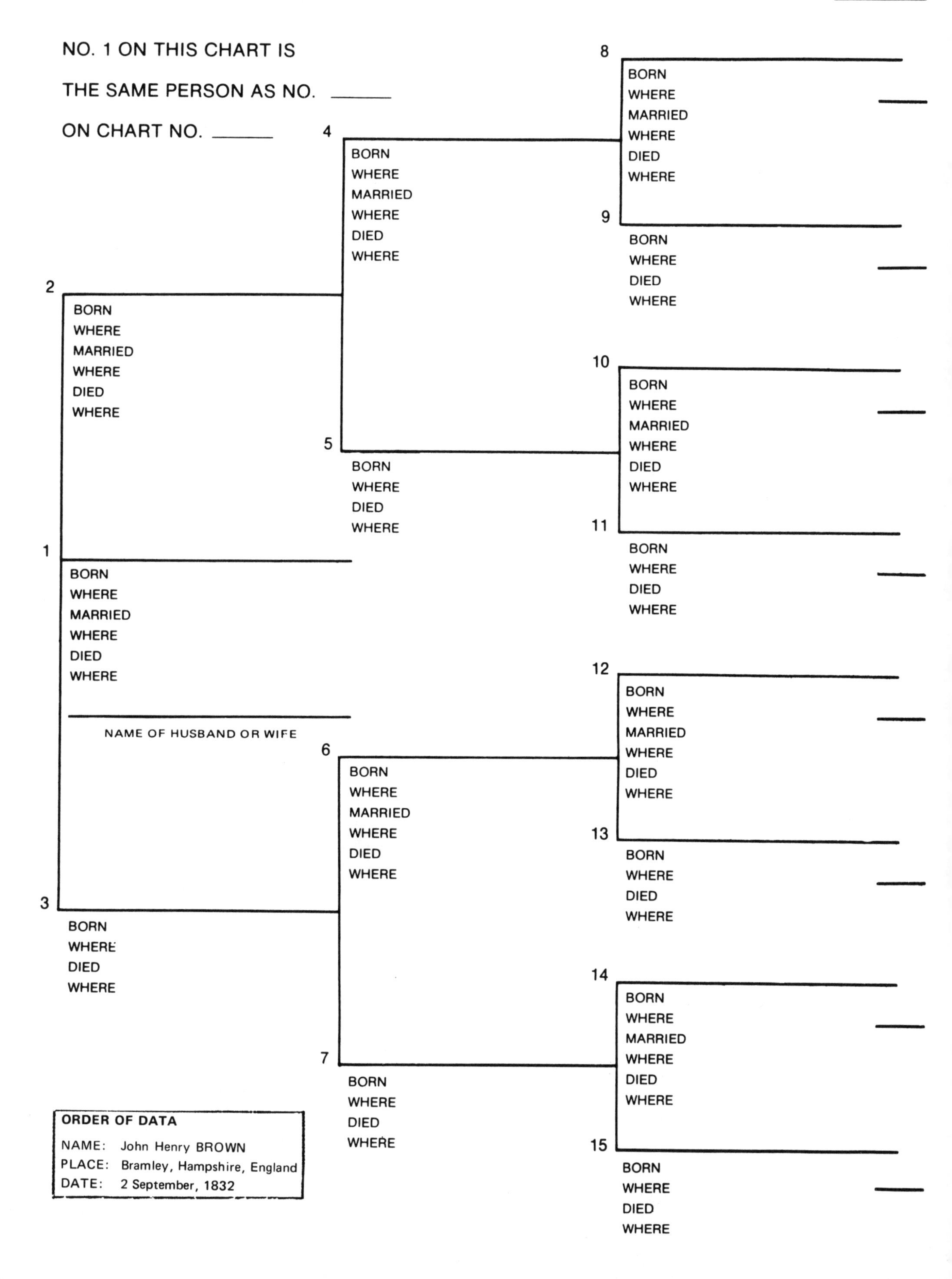

NO. 1 ON THIS CHART IS
THE SAME PERSON AS NO. ______
ON CHART NO. ______

2
BORN
WHERE
MARRIED
WHERE
DIED
WHERE

1
BORN
WHERE
MARRIED
WHERE
DIED
WHERE

NAME OF HUSBAND OR WIFE

3
BORN
WHERE
DIED
WHERE

4
BORN
WHERE
MARRIED
WHERE
DIED
WHERE

5
BORN
WHERE
DIED
WHERE

6
BORN
WHERE
MARRIED
WHERE
DIED
WHERE

7
BORN
WHERE
DIED
WHERE

8
BORN
WHERE
MARRIED
WHERE
DIED
WHERE

9
BORN
WHERE
DIED
WHERE

10
BORN
WHERE
MARRIED
WHERE
DIED
WHERE

11
BORN
WHERE
DIED
WHERE

12
BORN
WHERE
MARRIED
WHERE
DIED
WHERE

13
BORN
WHERE
DIED
WHERE

14
BORN
WHERE
MARRIED
WHERE
DIED
WHERE

15
BORN
WHERE
DIED
WHERE

**ORDER OF DATA**

NAME: John Henry BROWN
PLACE: Bramley, Hampshire, England
DATE: 2 September, 1832

# PEDIGREE CHART

CHART NO. ______

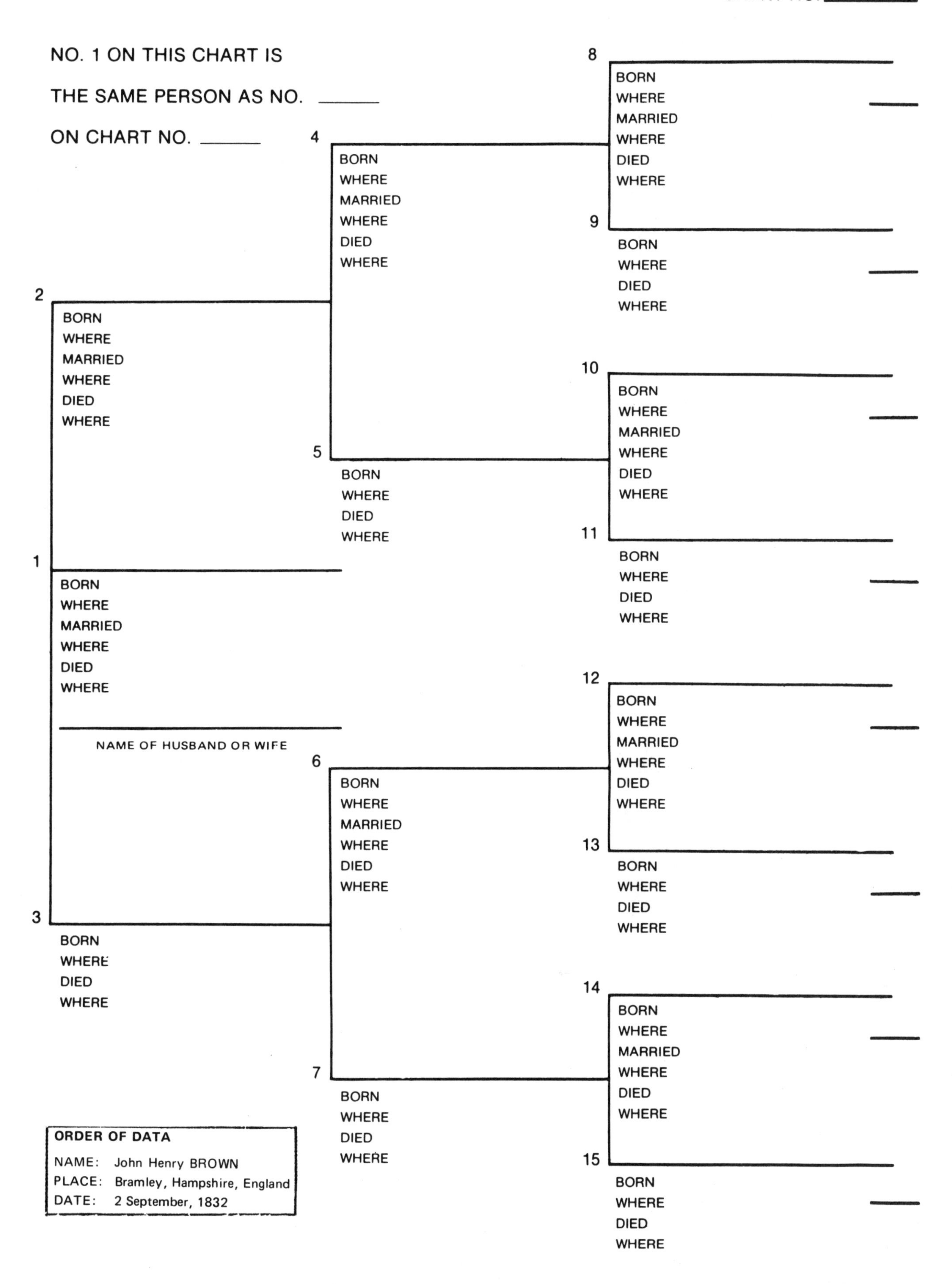

NO. 1 ON THIS CHART IS

THE SAME PERSON AS NO. ______

ON CHART NO. ______

8
BORN
WHERE
MARRIED
WHERE
DIED
WHERE

4
BORN
WHERE
MARRIED
WHERE
DIED
WHERE

9
BORN
WHERE
DIED
WHERE

2
BORN
WHERE
MARRIED
WHERE
DIED
WHERE

10
BORN
WHERE
MARRIED
WHERE
DIED
WHERE

5
BORN
WHERE
DIED
WHERE

11
BORN
WHERE
DIED
WHERE

1
BORN
WHERE
MARRIED
WHERE
DIED
WHERE

NAME OF HUSBAND OR WIFE

12
BORN
WHERE
MARRIED
WHERE
DIED
WHERE

6
BORN
WHERE
MARRIED
WHERE
DIED
WHERE

13
BORN
WHERE
DIED
WHERE

3
BORN
WHERE
DIED
WHERE

14
BORN
WHERE
MARRIED
WHERE
DIED
WHERE

7
BORN
WHERE
DIED
WHERE

15
BORN
WHERE
DIED
WHERE

**ORDER OF DATA**

NAME: John Henry BROWN
PLACE: Bramley, Hampshire, England
DATE: 2 September, 1832

# PEDIGREE CHART

CHART NO. ________

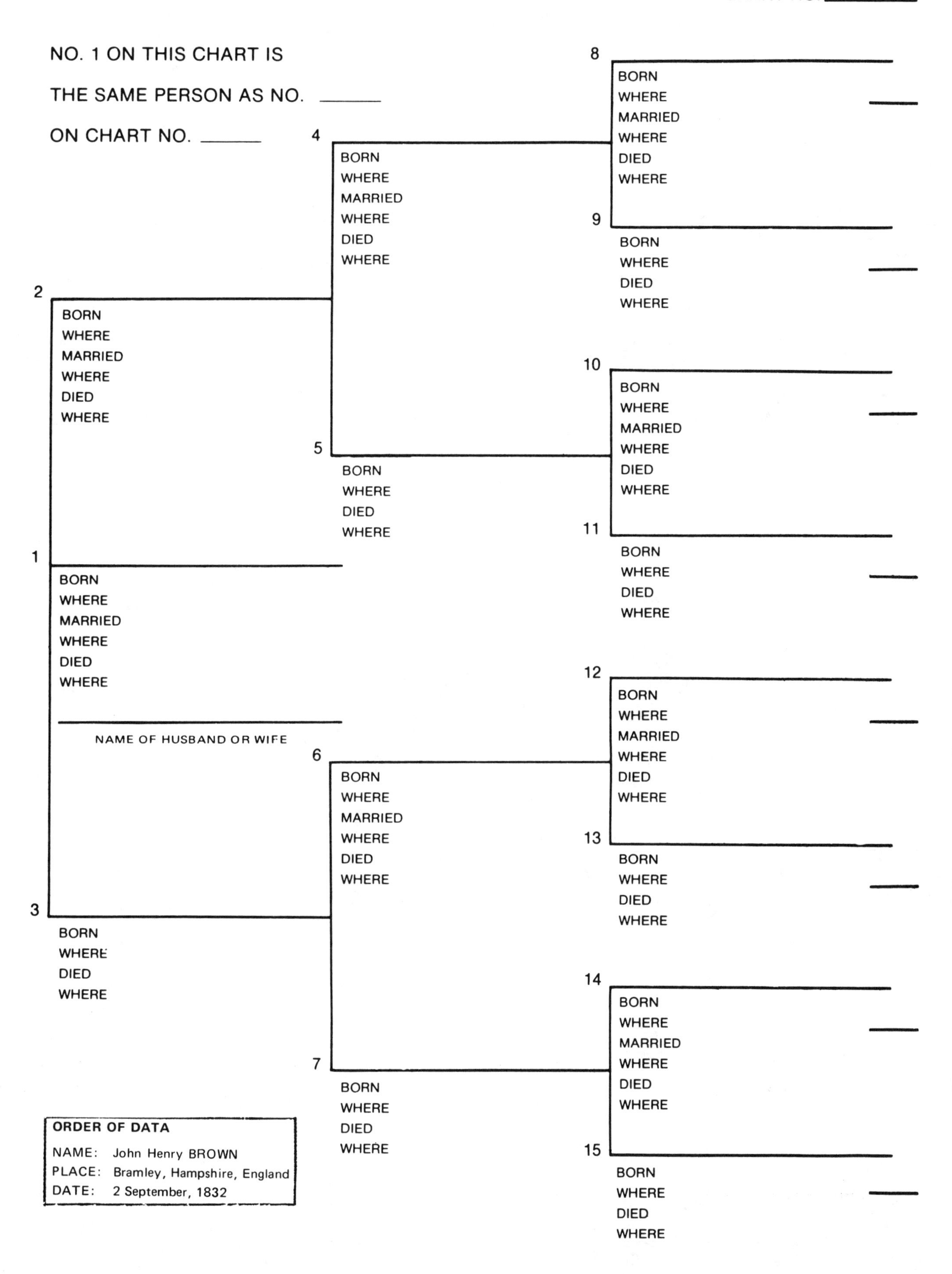

NO. 1 ON THIS CHART IS

THE SAME PERSON AS NO. ______

ON CHART NO. ______

2
BORN
WHERE
MARRIED
WHERE
DIED
WHERE

1
BORN
WHERE
MARRIED
WHERE
DIED
WHERE

NAME OF HUSBAND OR WIFE

3
BORN
WHERE
DIED
WHERE

4
BORN
WHERE
MARRIED
WHERE
DIED
WHERE

5
BORN
WHERE
DIED
WHERE

6
BORN
WHERE
MARRIED
WHERE
DIED
WHERE

7
BORN
WHERE
DIED
WHERE

8
BORN
WHERE
MARRIED
WHERE
DIED
WHERE

9
BORN
WHERE
DIED
WHERE

10
BORN
WHERE
MARRIED
WHERE
DIED
WHERE

11
BORN
WHERE
DIED
WHERE

12
BORN
WHERE
MARRIED
WHERE
DIED
WHERE

13
BORN
WHERE
DIED
WHERE

14
BORN
WHERE
MARRIED
WHERE
DIED
WHERE

15
BORN
WHERE
DIED
WHERE

**ORDER OF DATA**

NAME: John Henry BROWN
PLACE: Bramley, Hampshire, England
DATE: 2 September, 1832

# PEDIGREE CHART

CHART NO. ______

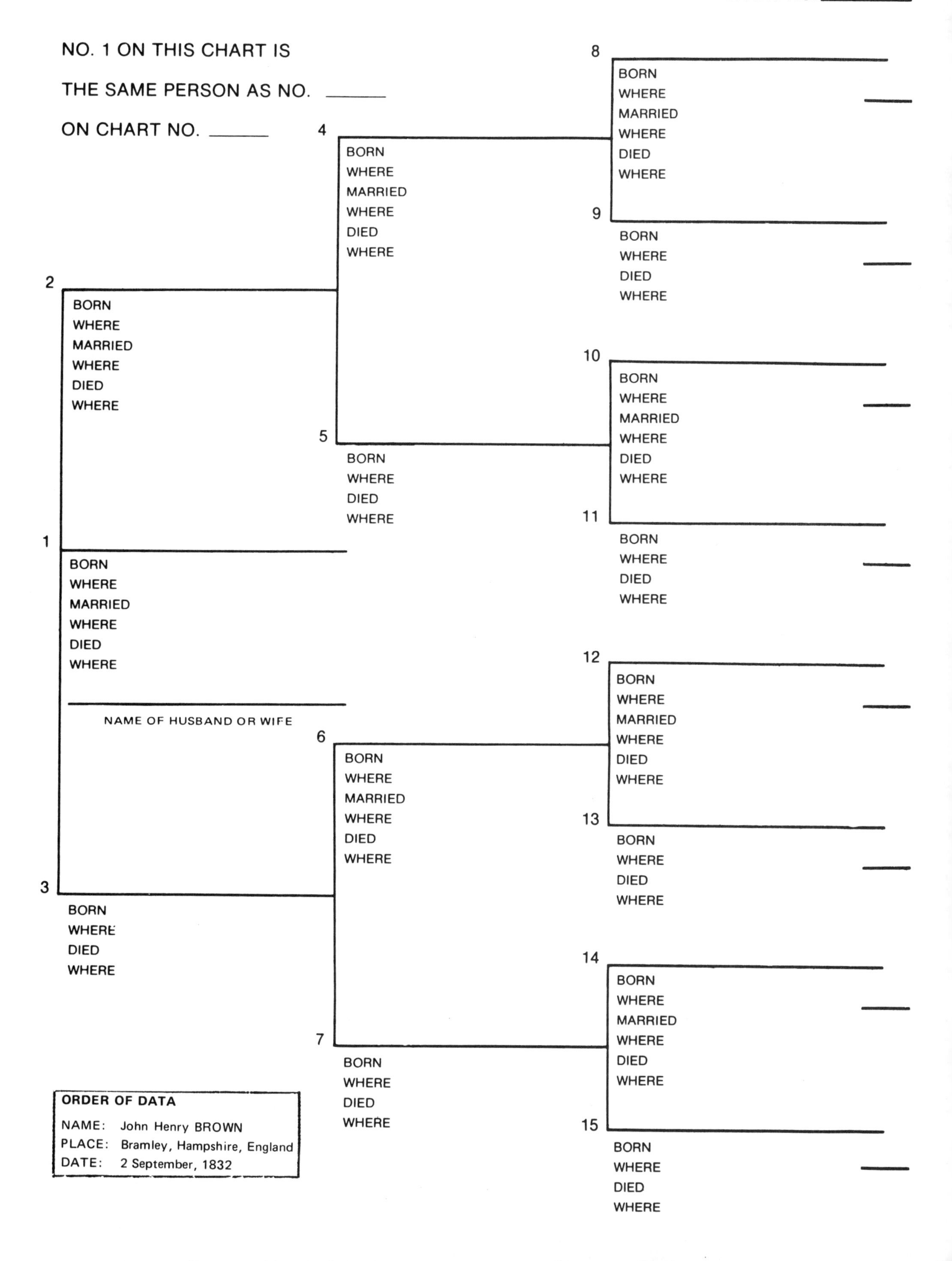

NO. 1 ON THIS CHART IS

THE SAME PERSON AS NO. ______

ON CHART NO. ______

8
BORN
WHERE
MARRIED
WHERE
DIED
WHERE

4
BORN
WHERE
MARRIED
WHERE
DIED
WHERE

9
BORN
WHERE
DIED
WHERE

2
BORN
WHERE
MARRIED
WHERE
DIED
WHERE

10
BORN
WHERE
MARRIED
WHERE
DIED
WHERE

5
BORN
WHERE
DIED
WHERE

11
BORN
WHERE
DIED
WHERE

1
BORN
WHERE
MARRIED
WHERE
DIED
WHERE

NAME OF HUSBAND OR WIFE

12
BORN
WHERE
MARRIED
WHERE
DIED
WHERE

6
BORN
WHERE
MARRIED
WHERE
DIED
WHERE

13
BORN
WHERE
DIED
WHERE

3
BORN
WHERE
DIED
WHERE

14
BORN
WHERE
MARRIED
WHERE
DIED
WHERE

7
BORN
WHERE
DIED
WHERE

15
BORN
WHERE
DIED
WHERE

**ORDER OF DATA**

NAME: John Henry BROWN
PLACE: Bramley, Hampshire, England
DATE: 2 September, 1832

# PEDIGREE CHART

CHART NO. ______

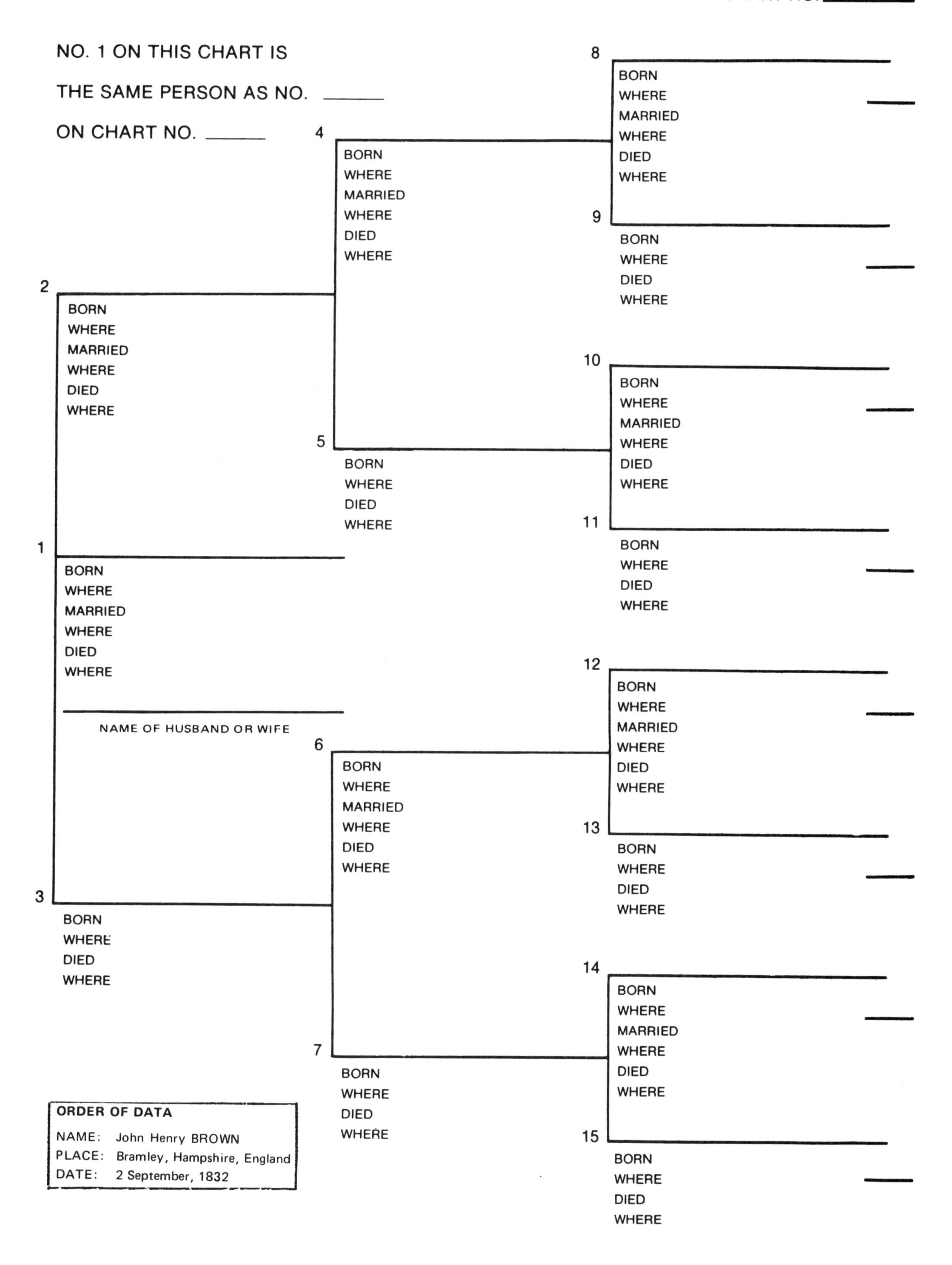

# PEDIGREE CHART

CHART NO. ________

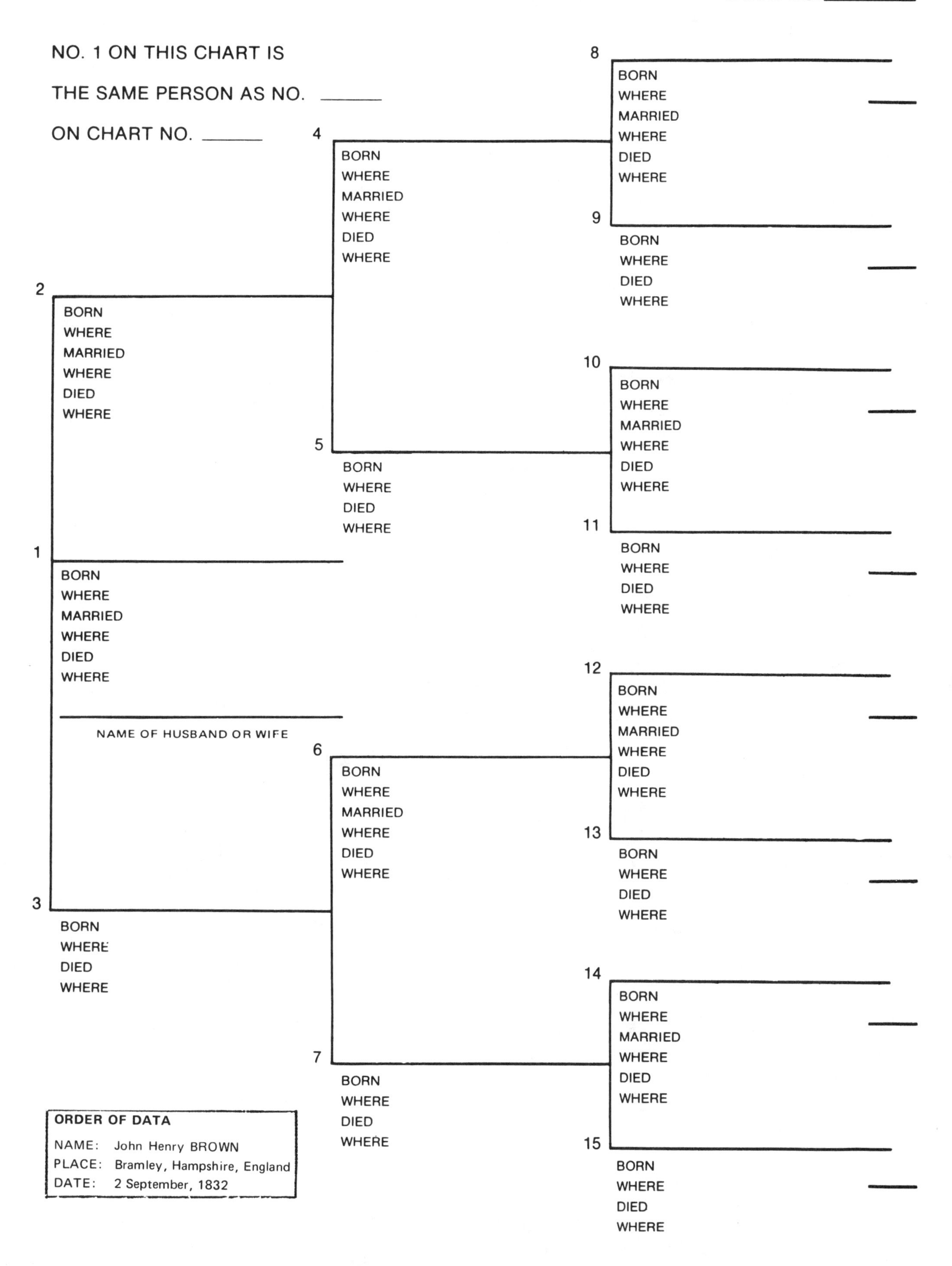

NO. 1 ON THIS CHART IS
THE SAME PERSON AS NO. ______
ON CHART NO. ______

8
BORN
WHERE
MARRIED
WHERE
DIED
WHERE

4
BORN
WHERE
MARRIED
WHERE
DIED
WHERE

9
BORN
WHERE
DIED
WHERE

2
BORN
WHERE
MARRIED
WHERE
DIED
WHERE

10
BORN
WHERE
MARRIED
WHERE
DIED
WHERE

5
BORN
WHERE
DIED
WHERE

11
BORN
WHERE
DIED
WHERE

1
BORN
WHERE
MARRIED
WHERE
DIED
WHERE

NAME OF HUSBAND OR WIFE

12
BORN
WHERE
MARRIED
WHERE
DIED
WHERE

6
BORN
WHERE
MARRIED
WHERE
DIED
WHERE

13
BORN
WHERE
DIED
WHERE

3
BORN
WHERE
DIED
WHERE

14
BORN
WHERE
MARRIED
WHERE
DIED
WHERE

7
BORN
WHERE
DIED
WHERE

15
BORN
WHERE
DIED
WHERE

ORDER OF DATA
NAME: John Henry BROWN
PLACE: Bramley, Hampshire, England
DATE: 2 September, 1832

## PEDIGREE CHART

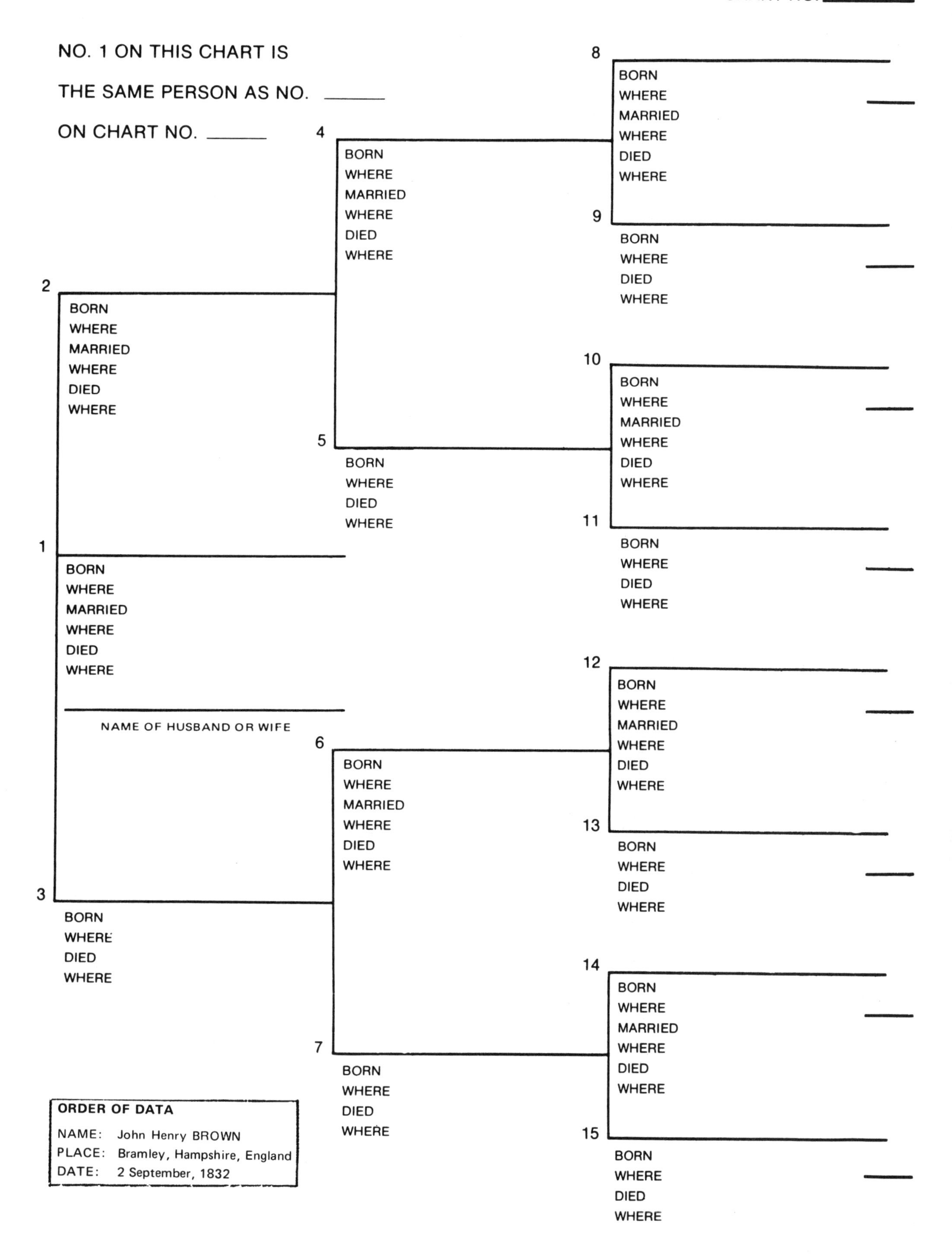